D0908518

THE DEPTH OF COLD

NEW SCIENCE SERIES

General Editor

SIR GRAHAM SUTTON, C.B.E., D.Sc., F.R.S.
Chairman of the National Environmental Council.

THE DEPTH
OF COLD

A. R. MEETHAM
D.Sc.

BARNES & NOBLE Inc.
NEW YORK
PUBLISHERS AND BOOKSELLERS SINCE 1873

Published in the United States, 1967
by Barnes & Noble, Inc.

Printed in Great Britain
by Hazell Watson & Viney Ltd., Aylesbury, Bucks

EDITOR'S FOREWORD

New Science Series

THE aim of the New Science Series is to provide authoritative accounts of topics chosen from the wide range of modern science. The series includes books by experts in the physical, biological and social sciences. In the selection of titles and in the treatment the needs of the reader who has a lively curiosity about the world around him, and is prepared to make a conscious effort to understand the thoughts and achievements of specialists, have been kept to the fore. Although special attention has been given to the younger generation, it is hoped that the series will also be of interest and value to more mature minds.

These books have been written to attract a wide audience. In an age in which life is increasingly affected by scientific discovery it seems essential that the practitioners should endeavour to make clear, in part if not in whole, the aims and implications of their work. It is hoped that the New Science Series will make a contribution to this end.

O.G.S.

AUTHOR'S PREFACE

THIS book is an introduction to low temperatures, as they affect everyday life, as well as technology and science. If it had been a symposium, instead of a solo effort, it might have had contributions from soldiers, sailors, railway porters, shopkeepers, physicians, surgeons, biologists, chemists, engineers, gas fitters and truck drivers, besides the inevitable meteorologists and physicists.

My own interests in cold are both technical and scientific. First as a meteorologist concerned with the upper atmosphere I found low temperatures, as it were, in the raw. Later when working with atmospheric pollution I wondered why the most unpleasant fogs seemed to occur when the temperature was neither much above nor much below freezing point. Later still I made hydrogen, neon and helium liquefiers at the National Physical Laboratory and helped to provide cold liquids for research on metals, computers and chemical energy.

In a way, we are now the masters of low temperatures, as we have mastered radio communication, for example, and we are turning them effectively to our own use. On the other hand, we still have a long way to go theoretically: we still have no clear idea of how heat is conducted, or even of what temperature "really" is. We can make ourselves a snug space capsule to live in, or a comfortable shelter at the South Pole, but we still cannot control, or forecast far in advance, the approach of severe winter weather. We are living in an Ice Age, but we are still trying to find the reason for ice ages. It has been my aim in this book to show how wide we have already made the field of low temperatures, and also to show what we are up against before we can make it wider still.

I should like to thank Dr. John S. Hill for his help in improving parts of this book. His doctor's thesis reported measurements with radioactive decay of materials in very strong magnetic fields at 0·01 degree above absolute zero.

A. R. M.

Highgate,
London, N.6.
December 1966

CONTENTS

Chapter One

EXTREMES

PEOPLE TRAVEL for all sorts of reasons—to visit friends, relatives or colleagues, to study other people's artistic achievements and ways of life, or simply to take a holiday, perhaps to develop a good sun-tan or enjoy winter sports. Some go for adventure, others simply to get away from the narrowness or boredom of their everyday existence. In comparison with these often excellent reasons it would be eccentric, but at least purposeful, to travel simply in search of low temperatures. This is what we are now going to do, in imagination, and some of our ports of call will certainly not be found in the glossy brochures of the travel agencies.

As it happens, the first place on the list is a well known spa. In an English winter, the best choice of a traveller in search of cold seems to be Buxton, Derbyshire, where on 11th February, 1885, the English record low temperature of −11°F was reached. The corresponding choice for Scotland is Braemar, where −17°F was recorded on the same night—it was during the severest frost experienced in these islands in the last hundred years. For Wales the record is held by Rhayader (−10°F on 21st January, 1940) and for Ireland by Marku Castle (−2°F on 16th January, 1861). For London the minimum is about zero (+1°F on 5th January, 1867).

All these measurements were made with certificated thermometers inside carefully designed boxes with louvred openings on all four sides. There was an even lower temperature reported at Blackadder, East Berwickshire, on 4th December, 1879, six degrees colder than the official United Kingdom record, but the thermometer was uncertified and its accuracy was in doubt. Moreover the louvred box containing it was fixed to a wall, instead of standing above level grass-covered soil. This is the standard method of exposure, with thermometer bulb 4 ft above ground, so that the measured temperature is representative of the general air of a neighbourhood. One often hears a weather forecast referring to "ground frost" with little possibility of "air frost", particularly if the night is expected to be cloudless. This brings out the point that even in extremely cold weather the general air may not be the coldest object. The wall and nearby ground at Blackadder could have been excessively cold that night, through radiation of their heat to a cloudless sky. A pocket of exceptionally cold air might then have accumulated, some of it entering the thermometer screen and producing an unrepresentative temperature reading.

There must be many places in the British Isles where lower temperatures have been reached than those which stand as the records, but where there was no reliable thermometer to record them. Since our eccentric traveller would be able to take his own thermometer and screen with him he might prefer to try districts where there are no regular observing stations. High up in the Cairngorms would be a good idea, or perhaps in that case he might choose somewhere in Glenlivet, Banffshire, about midway between Aberdeen and Inverness as the crow flies. Here in 1947 there was the longest unbroken frost on record; 25 consecutive days from 26th January to 19th February. There were slight thaws on 19th and 20th February, and then the frost continued until 2nd March, making a total of 36 days. Many people all over the country remember that cold spell, including the National Coal Board, and the gas and electricity industries, who could not supply enough fuel to keep the people warm.

But no one in search of really low temperatures would waste time in the British Isles, surrounded by sea which never even freezes. For real winter cold, over a million square miles of land is needed, covered by snow or ice. Once the snow has covered such an area, it sets up a weather situation in which the area and the air above it turn progressively colder still. Even if the sun shines by day, the snow reflects most of its heat away. By night, the snow effectively radiates heat into outer space. This might have been conserved if there had been plenty of moisture in the air, but air that is already cold can hold very little moisture.

Above large snow covered areas of land, fairly permanent anticyclones develop. This means that pressure is high, and winds are light, drifting outwards and spreading the colder area still further. The cloud amount is small because there is little evaporation to restock the dry air with moisture. Low pressure areas, with strong winds and moisture-laden air, are held away and travel round the anticyclone at a radius of many hundreds of miles.

In the northern hemisphere two great anticyclones turn up over land regularly every winter. They are centred over eastern Siberia and north-west Canada. Here are where the coldest places will be found, and any town in the neighbouring part of the continent is likely to come under the anticyclonic influence and suffer very severe winters. In the southern hemisphere the only land high pressure area in winter is over Antarctica and the South Pole, and this is where the coldest climate of all is found.

We may first look at some of the records which have been tabulated in the weather books and the *Guinness Book of Records*. Moscow, for instance, is the coldest big city, with an extreme minimum of −43·6°F in January 1940. In the U.S.A. the record is held by Rogers Pass, Montana, with −70°F on 20th January, 1954. More strictly it belongs to Tanana, Alaska, with −76°F in January 1886. Nearby at Snag Airport in the Canadian part of the Yukon river mining area, the lowest so far is −81°F on 3rd February, 1947.

For many years the world record was held jointly by two places in north-east Siberia, with −90·4°F. One of these, Verkhoyansk, is an important centre and gives its name to a mountain range about as big as Great Britain. The other, Oimyekon, is at a much higher altitude in the same mountains but it is not even inside the Arctic Circle. The lowest temperature observation there was made fairly recently on 1st February, 1933.

Expeditions towards the North Pole have not so far encountered lower temperatures. For example, on the Greenland Ice Cap, at an altitude of 9,280 ft, −84·6°F was found. It is towards the South Pole that we must go to find the lowest temperatures yet observed on the earth's surface. In 1957–58 there was a great scientific survey of the whole world and its atmosphere, a co-operative effort by the scientists of all countries. It was planned in advance with extreme care; for instance meteorological balloons were sent up simultaneously all over the world on eighty days during the 19 months' period, and every conceivable type of observation from magnetic variations and aurorae to radio atmospherics and meteors was taken at the same time. Even by 1963 not all the results had been worked out.

This international piece of research was called the I.G.Y., or

International Geophysical Year. There had been earlier exercises of a similar kind in 1882–83 and 1902–03, but this one was much larger and more thoroughly instrumented than the other two. Moreover, with modern means of transport including snow tractors, aeroplanes and helicopters, it was possible to set up well equipped and tolerably comfortable stations at a number of places on the Antarctic Ice Cap. Even the "Pole of Inaccessibility" was visited; this is the point on the Antarctic continent which is hardest to reach by land, from whichever direction you try to approach it.

Two Russian-manned bases in Antarctica recorded the lowest minimum temperatures of all. They were −125·3°F on 25th August, 1958 at the base Vostok (altitude 10,400 ft), and −117·4°F on 25th June, 1958 at Sovietskaya (altitude 11,300 ft). At the South Pole itself the base was named the Amundsen-Scott I.G.Y. Station after the two explorers who reached the South Pole within five weeks of each other in December 1911 and January 1912. Here the lowest temperature recorded by the international party who wintered there in the I.G.Y. was −102·1F on 18th September, 1957.

Eccentric as our cold-seeking traveller is, he may still fight shy of chartering a polar expedition to realize his ambition. Can he do better by travelling upward? Perhaps some mountain top accessible by chair-lift will reach a low enough temperature? This possibility can be settled in some degree by calculation, founded on observations such as those made by the hardy Scottish meteorologists who lived at the top of Ben Nevis during the period 1884-93. Their lowest recorded temperature was +0·7°F, but they found that on an average Ben Nevis was 15·7°F colder than Fort William on the shore of the loch below. The difference in altitude between the two stations was 4,234 ft, corresponding to a drop of 1°F for every 270 ft of altitude. Later observations with thermometers on kites and balloons led to the average value of 1°F for every 280 ft, and this will be the basis of our present calculations.

If we start with Mt Everest, we may use the fact that Lhasa in Tibet at an altitude of 13,000 ft has a minimum of +3°F. Everest is 16,000 ft higher and therefore 16,000/280 = 57° colder; so its minimum should be around   54°F. Approximately the same answer is reached by starting from the minimum temperature in the plains of Bihar. The Northern Rockies are much colder than this. Mt McKinley at 20,300 ft towers above Snag Airport, but it must benefit a great deal from the strong warming effect of the North Pacific ocean. It would be unwise to take Snag's reading of −81°F as the basis of the calculation; a more appropriate figure would be −50°F, on which basis the top of McKinley will reach −122°F. No other peak in the Rockies, even though it is much further away from the sea, will reach so low a temperature.

The same formula of 1°F for 280 ft of altitude leads to even lower estimates of minimum temperatures in other parts of the world. Gora Chen, of altitude 10,217 ft in the mountains near Verkhoyansk gets an estimate of −125°F, and the 20,000 ft peaks in Antarctica would be estimated to have the fantastically low temperature of −160°F.

According to these speculations, our eccentric traveller would still have to organize an Antarctic expedition, and include in his equipment the ropes, tents and oxygen cylinders of Himalayan climbers as well. But one very important point has been overlooked. The reduction of temperature with altitude does not continue indefinitely. As we ascend from any place on the earth's surface, we always reach a level in the atmosphere where the temperature stops falling. Higher up still, it usually remains more or less steady, but it may even rise a little to begin with.

At different levels in the two curves there is an abrupt change. The region where this occurs is called the tropopause. Beneath it, the air is circulating violently with the winds, clouds, thunderstorms and weather phenomena we are accustomed to seeing. Above it, the air, which is very much rarefied, is warmed directly by radiation from both the sun and the earth.

As will be seen in Fig. 1, temperatures below −130°F should never be experienced in the atmosphere up to heights of 80,000 ft. On the other hand, the figure makes no allowance for the effects of mountains. It might be argued that a very cold wind blowing up the mountain slopes of Antarctica is a special case; that the cooling effect of such air as it rushes uphill and expands is unavoidable, even with the help of radiation effects; and that in fact the tropopause must be driven upwards by these mountain winds. It is therefore arguable that the eccentric traveller, if he stayed long enough on an Antarctic peak, might possibly experience a temperature as low as −160°F.

If he will be content with a guaranteed temperature of $-120°F$ or so, he will save a great deal of money by organizing a balloon ascent instead of a polar expedition. Fig. 1 shows that a balloon rising from equatorial regions will be in air of this temperature

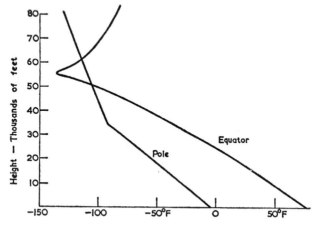

Fig. 1.1. Typical variations of temperature with height in polar regions, and near the equator.

when it reaches a height of 50,000 ft or about 9 miles. Such an ascent can easily be made and the return journey to earth completed in 3 hours.

Our traveller had better not make the mistake of the famous meteorologist James Glaisher, who, in 1862, made an ascent of 7 miles in an open basket. An engraving in his own book describing his balloon adventures shows him, a grey haired, side-whiskered, handsome man in his fifties, wearing a scarf, but no overcoat or gloves, unconscious in his basket. Three feet above him in the rigging is H. Coxwell, his balloonist, disentangling the rope of the valve for releasing hydrogen from the balloon. Coxwell's hands became frozen and useless, but he made good use of his elbows and teeth, and the balloon brought them safely down. Its minimum thermometer read $-119°F$, corresponding to a maximum height of 37,000 ft.

Glaisher had fainted through lack of oxygen, the air pressure being only a quarter of the normal pressure at the ground.

Within one or two minutes of recovering consciousness he was using his instruments again to take readings of temperature, pressure and humidity. His altitude record was not broken until 1931 by Professor Piccard who travelled in a sealed metal gondola. The highest manned balloon flight of all time was that of the American Explorer II in 1934, which rose to 72,395 ft, high enough for the curvature of the earth to be photographed. These heights can now be reached by aircraft, and greatly exceeded by manned satellites.

We may now imagine that our eccentric traveller has flown 9 miles over the equator, and has spent a winter on his chosen peak in the Antarctic. Where can he go next? He will probably have to wait many years unless he enlists for duty in an American or Russian space-research project. Then he may be able to travel to the moon and the planets, and achieve some truly remarkable readings with his thermometer.

Although man has not yet sent a thermometer to other planets, the astronomers have made estimates of their temperatures, after measuring the heat and radio waves they emit. The moon, Venus and Mars are near enough for measurements to be made of the emissions from different parts of their surface, and consequently the estimated temperatures are more specific than those of the remaining planets.

Temperatures of the moon and the planets:

Moon	215° F (sunlit side)	−243°F (dark side)
Mercury	645°F (average)	
Venus	586°F (surface)	−37°F (upper atmosphere)
Earth	−125°F	
Mars	81°F (summer)	−190°F (winter)
Jupiter	−202°F (average)	
Saturn	−270°F	
Uranus	less than −280°F	
Neptune	−265°F	
Pluto	−350°F	

As might be expected the planet most distant from the sun (and from the earth) has the lowest temperature. To find colder places than Pluto, the traveller would have to go far out into space, where the sun appears no bigger than the other stars, and he would take many years, perhaps a whole lifetime, to get there. Even then, if he had the wrong kind of thermometer, he would get a disappointing result. Interstellar space is not completely empty of matter, though it contains less matter than the best vacuum we can make on earth. It contains between one and ten atoms of gas per cubic centimetre, and these atoms have velocities corresponding to a temperature of about $-280°F$. If the thermometer were influenced by these gaseous atoms, its reading would not be as low as on Pluto. On the other hand, if the thermometer were influenced only by the radiation from the stars and other material in space, it would read $-453°F$.

We know of no place in the universe colder than this, except the experimental spaces in our own low temperature laboratories, about a hundred of them in the whole world. Here will be found experiments in which matter is cooled to $-459·6°F$. Moreover, very much more interesting things are going on there than in the coldest regions of space.

Here is one strange oddity, just to be going on with. No physicist would dare to claim that he had reached a temperature even a tenth of a degree lower than the figure quoted just above: his colleagues would merely laugh at him. This is because it was proved long ago that, although there is no upper limit of temperature, there is a hard and fast lower limit. In this book we shall examine what cold is, how it is produced, what good and harm it does, and what uses we can make of it. The investigation is not an easy one, because it takes us into some of the most difficult regions of both classical and modern physics.

Chapter Two

HEAT

IF A DICTIONARY were available of the first twenty or so words ever to be used by prehistoric man, it would include words meaning "hot" and "cold" to be used as adjectives describing states of the human body and of objects which could be touched. But the words are not what they seem. We all now know, what physicists have understood since Victorian times, that they refer to temperature, and only quite indirectly to heat, and that heat and temperature are utterly different from each other.

Both these concepts have had so much written about them that their story ought to be complete, but it is not even nearly complete. Both heat and temperature are still subjects of experiment and debate. Both have altered in significance within the last few years, and even today no scientist would be bold enough to claim that he understands them perfectly, or to predict that anyone will do so in the foreseeable future.

It will be necessary to look quite carefully at the concept of heat, although this book is primarily about temperature, and low temperature at that. Why? The short answer is simply that we shall be concerned with ways of making objects cold. This can only be done by taking heat out of them. Normally, if it is necessary to take heat out of one object, we just let it flow into another, colder object. But what do we do when there is no colder available object? Something can indeed be done, but only by skilful use of modern knowledge of heat. The branch of science needed for this purpose is well named. It is *thermodynamics*, the science of the relation between heat and mechanical work.

Heat as a Fluid

Whenever you lie in the sun or put a cold hand into warm water you can feel heat soaking into you. This is the most obvious property of heat, that it flows, like a fluid. The ancient Greeks thought that heat was indeed a fluid, but not an ordinary one. It was "imponderable" because it could not be collected and

weighed or otherwise examined. They thought that heat was the
essence of fire; warm bodies possessed more of it than cold ones;
ice had to absorb it in order to melt; and, very erroneously, they
thought that combustible materials such as wood also possessed the
essence of fire in another form, and this enabled them to burn.
All these ideas fitted into their belief that everything is composed
of various mixtures of four "elements", earth, air, fire and
water.

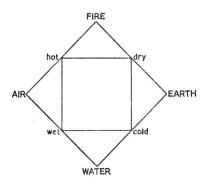

Fig. 2.1. The Greek elements.

The Greek concept of elements was accepted as completely
satisfactory, by all except a few people like Francis Bacon, until
about 1800, when John Dalton showed good reason why we
should think of matter as made up of the *chemical* elements,
hydrogen, oxygen, carbon and so on. Water was shown to be a
compound of two elements. The Earths or ashes that were left
after substances had been burned were other compounds. The
Airs or gases could be elements or compounds, or mixtures like
the air we breathe. The true science of chemistry was taking
shape, and only Fire remained a mystery.

For a century after Dalton, heat remained almost where the
Greeks had left it, but with a few elaborations. It was a fluid, but
an indestructible, uncreatable, highly elastic, self-repellent, all
pervading fluid. It was called "caloric". Let there be no mis-
conception, however. The theory of caloric provided sensible and
logical explanations of nearly all the properties of heat then
known, especially those in which the flow of heat was involved.

Heat as Energy

We now know that the atoms and molecules which Dalton revealed to science are much more than the simple building blocks of chemistry. They have complicated structure, electrical and magnetic properties, and the ability to interact with light and other forms of radiation. Above all, they have energy, part of which is the energy of motion. The molecules of a liquid or a gas can be seen to be in motion in careful experiments using microscopes. Even the atoms in solids are in motion, and though they are much more cribbed and confined than those of gases and liquids, they possess just as much actual energy as their unbound brethren.

An atom or molecule can have its energy in various forms: *kinetic*—energy of motion in a straight line; *rotational*—energy of spin; and *vibrational*—energy due to distortion or displacement from a rest position. The total energy in all three forms in any single molecule is extremely small. On the other hand there is an extremely large number of molecules in any handleable piece of matter, and the total energy of all the molecules turns out to be quite large. This total energy of the molecules in a body is called the heat in the body.

Our modern idea or "model" of heat has one disadvantage compared with the Greek model: it makes the flow of heat rather difficult to explain in mathematical detail (in point of fact the Greeks avoided having to explain it by a plain tautology). Among its many advantages, however, the modern energy model of heat has the ability to deal easily with measurement of heat. It is fully accurate on problems about heat engines and refrigeration, whereas the old caloric model would be utterly lost.

Measurement of Heat

The caloric model was doomed from the time when people began to measure heat systematically. One very good way of doing this, which is still used in research today, was to measure heat in terms of the amount of ice it would melt. A more general way, of great experimental value, had been made possible in the mid-seventeenth century by the invention of thermometers. These measure temperature, which is definitely not heat; we shall see what it is in Chapter Four. However, thermometers and tem-

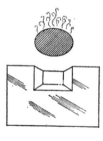

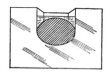

Fig. 2.2. Measuring heat in terms of the amount of ice it will melt.

perature are so familiar to everybody nowadays that we can conveniently skip the philosophy for the present, and think in terms of an ordinary centigrade thermometer which reads 0°C in melting ice and 100°C in boiling water at standard atmospheric pressure.

Using thermometers, people could investigate what happens when two "bodies" of different temperatures are brought together. For instance, if a one-ounce brass weight is heated to 100°C and lowered into a glass of cold water, this will rise in temperature by a few degrees. If the same thing is done with a two-ounce weight the temperature of the water will rise nearly, but not quite, twice as much. In fact, the heat lost by the brass is in both cases exactly equal to the heat gained by the water. In the second case, the two-ounce weight did not have to cool quite so much, because the final temperature of the water (and the brass) was higher.

This kind of measurement, made much more carefully, led to the introduction of fixed units of heat, in terms of which all quantities of heat could be measured. There were and still are various alternative units of heat. One of the most important was called the calorie, and defined as the heat necessary to raise the temperature of 1 gramme of water by 1°C.

Rumford and Joule

In 1798, Count Rumford measured the heat produced by friction, and gained support for the modern idea that heat is a form of molecular motion. It had been well known for a long time that whenever a gun barrel is drilled, both the gunmetal barrel and the hard steel of the drill became hot. Rumford measured the heat when a very blunt drill was used. When enough heat had been produced to boil 26·5 lb of water the powder from the drilling only weighed 9·5 oz. This amount of powder did not seem capable of carrying with it enough caloric to boil so much water, and when cool again, its capacity for heat was no different from ordinary gunmetal. Advocates of the caloric theory could still claim that some of the latent heat normally required for melting had manifested itself in the powder, but they were wrong, of course.

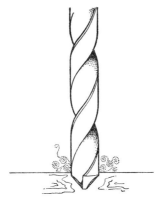

Fig. 2.3. Heat from a drill.

Usually when there is a clear-cut issue to be decided, a number of scientists get on the right track almost simultaneously, but this time much of the important work was done by one man, James Prescott Joule, owner of a Manchester brewery. Joule first found how to calculate the energy needed to drive an electric current through a resistance wire for a measured period of time. (This is C^2Rt, or *current squared* times *resistance* times *time*, and it is known as Joule's law.) He then put the resistance wire in water and found that the rise in temperature of the water was in proportion to the energy put in.

He thus showed that the heat received by the water was proportional to the energy put in. Heat was therefore likely to be just another form of energy, as indeed we now know. Joule went further. He measured the mechanical energy used to drive the dynamo generating the current to heat the water, and in 1840 he was able to demonstrate that an exact number of mechanical units of energy are required to produce a unit of heat. In later years he performed the famous experiment to measure directly the "mechanical equivalent" of heat. This showed that Rumford's calculations fifty years earlier from his crude gunmetal experiments had been accurate within about ten per cent. In round figures and modern units, it turned out that one calorie of heat was equivalent to 42 million ergs of mechanical energy. A cat uses about 420 million ergs, or 10 calories, when it jumps on to a 6 ft wall.

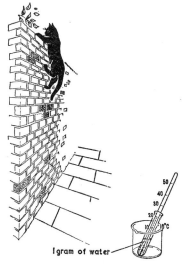

Fig. 2.4. 420 million ergs = 10 calories.

The First Law

Other forms of energy were also proved to be convertible into each other. Within the limits of accuracy obtainable at the time, electrical, mechanical, chemical, magnetic, potential, kinetic, in fact all known forms of energy were convertible without measurable loss into each other and into heat. People formulated a universal principle, that "energy can be neither created nor destroyed". Even with modern instruments of the highest precision of measurement, no exception has ever been found to this great unifying physical "law". It is called the principle of the Conservation of Energy or, whenever relating specially to heat, the First Law of Thermodynamics. We shall simply call it the First Law.

The usefulness of the First Law is this. If we make all the

proper measurements about any system and add them up we shall not find any changes at all in the total energy, however much the system changes within itself. Since in this book we are not going to do any actual calculations we may as well take a really difficult example. A steam engine burns 1 cwt of coal, boils 100 lb of water, emits into the air 100 lb of steam at 5 atmospheres pressure and 500 lb of hot smoky gases at 1·01 atmospheres pressure. It hauls a train of 500 tons for 1 mile up a gradient of 1 in 50 and accelerates it from rest to 20 miles per hour. The wheels, axles, bearings, rails and fireman all get warm and lose part of their heat to the air. The 50-volt service batteries on charge take in a net 10 ampere-hours during this time, but the lamps in the carriages use up 1 kWh. And so on. Many details are still missing from this tedious sum, but if all is properly measured and added up, the chemical energy in that 1 cwt of coal will be exactly equal to the total of all the other energies produced by its burning.

So heat is a form of energy. It is more like mechanical energy than any of the others, though it is uniquely different from all of them.

Kinetic Theory

The energy model of heat is most straightforward in the case of gases. When the late Victorians began to make mathematical models of gases, they supposed that the molecules of a gas were like perfect billiard balls, flying about in space, but not influenced by gravity. They collided with each other and with the walls of the vessel containing them, bouncing off with perfect elasticity. Temperature, pressure, density, viscosity, diffusion and many other properties of gases could be explained by the model. Heat was found to be simply the kinetic energy of the billiard balls, measured in terms of $\frac{1}{2}mv^2$, m being the mass of a ball, and v its velocity.

This idea of heat as kinetic energy, i.e. energy of motion, worked very well for gases like argon and helium, whose molecules are spherical like billiard balls. The energy needed to raise the temperature of such a gas by one degree came out right. But it came out too small in the case of gases like oxygen, whose molecules contain two atoms separated by a small but measurable distance.

When the separation between the atoms of such a molecule is

slightly increased, an attractive force brings the atoms closer again; when it is decreased, a strong repulsive force increases their separation. This is rather like the action of a spring, so the model makers tried supposing that an oxygen molecule was two

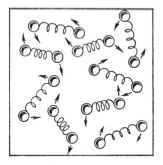

Fig. 2.5. Model of oxygen gas.

billiard balls joined together by a spring. They found that the calculated energy needed to increase the temperature of the gas came out more nearly right. If extra energy is put into a vessel containing model molecules of this type, three things can happen. First as before, a molecule can move faster. Second, the two balls

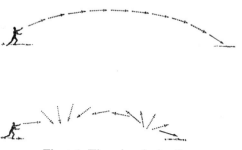

Fig. 2.6. Throwing the javelin.

can spin round each other; a little thought will convince you that energy is needed to set an object spinning—you can throw a heavy stick further if you throw it like a spear than if you let it rotate. Third, the two balls can oscillate towards and away from each other, alternately compressing and stretching the spring as they do so. When this happens, some of the energy is stored in the spring, in a form known as potential energy. There were mathematical reasons to show that any energy that was available had to be shared fairly equally, not only between "molecules", but between the linear, rotatory and vibratory forms of motion as well. So the Victorian model makers had to introduce spins and vibrations, as well as motion in straight lines, to make the model conform more closely with the facts of observation.

Spins and vibrations become even more important in models of liquids and solids, where there is no room for continuous motions

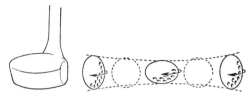

Fig. 2.7. Spin and vibration of a golf ball.

in straight lines. They are also used in quantum mechanics, and in the quantum models which have for many purposes replaced the earlier billiard ball models of matter. For the present, we can say that heat is a form of energy associated with motion of molecules, and of atoms within molecules, and leave it at that. Later on, we shall have to be more precise.

Chapter Three

SURVIVAL IN THE COLD

DURING ANY EXCEPTIONALLY long cold spell of weather, such as that of January and February 1963, we soon find how difficult it is to keep going when our economy has been designed for a milder climate. In Britain we very soon start examining our crude arrangements for coping with cold weather, in contrast with those of Germany, Switzerland, Austria, Russia, Canada and the United States. Our town streets become dangerous and dirty while local highways departments laboriously assemble equipment and labour forces to deal with accumulations of ice and snow. Domestic refuse piles up around the dustbins. The drain pipes down the outside walls of our houses freeze solid because a trickle of water from some tap or overflow turns to ice as it runs down the pipes. The water tanks freeze because our rather haphazard methods of house heating fail to reach them or the pipes leading from them. Plumbers find they have far more jobs than they can manage, and more friends than they ever knew. Soon the water companies' mains start freezing under the streets, and not even the one cold water tap in the kitchen can function. Standpipes appear in the streets, and muffled figures rush out to them and fill their buckets. Paving stones, lifted by frost-heave, trip the unwary pedestrian. Fuel becomes enormously important. Electric power voltages drop and television pictures turn dim or ridiculously small. Street lights flicker or go out as districts take it in turn to suffer power cuts. Hospitals and other vital services have to call for special power arrangements. Coal and gas supplies have to be rationed.

Outside the towns, people suddenly find themselves in a state of siege. Villages are cut off. Farm animals cannot be reached with their fodder. Coachloads and trainloads of passengers become stranded in remote areas of the countryside. Rescue operations are made by the police, the ambulance, road and fire services, the Army and R.A.F. helicopters. Diesel oil becomes treacly in the tanks of lorries and locomotives, and puts them out of action for days or weeks. Avalanches and snow drifts block roads and railways. Passenger trains are cancelled to make it possible for goods trains to run with essential freight, especially coal. Industrial activities are slowed down and unemployment figures mount upwards.

All these happenings are indeed grim, but they do not bring anyone except the extremely unfortunate few to face the stark facts of survival. There is a lot of grumbling, and the authorities are blamed for lack of foresight when they have probably known all along the risk they were taking in not having enough snow ploughs, steam engines and rescue services to deal with the worst possible situation. People live uncomfortably and inefficiently for a while, but then they return to their normal lives rather pleased to have been through such an incident.

There are nevertheless situations where one's chances of survival are slim, and where every calorie of heat and strength must be conserved as long as possible. Perhaps luckily, such situations usually descend on people who know the risks they are taking, such as troopers, explorers and mountaineers. They at least have had opportunities to prepare themselves. All the same, the experience of these specialists may suddenly become important to ordinary people. In severe weather, any outdoor workers, including railway staff, delivery men, postmen, farmers and lorry drivers, may find themselves in trouble. Any motorist, even, may have to spend a night in a snowdrift. So what are the best preparations to make, and what measures of first aid should be given to victims ?

The experiences of World War II have been published in a book[1] and they show that important principles of physics, as well as of medicine, are involved. Suppose you are standing out of doors, well wrapped up, on a cold windy day. Your survival task is to supply enough heat inside your body to keep at least your vital organs warm. They work best at 98·6°F, but if you are strong and healthy they will continue to work at 98·0°F or even for short periods at 97·0°F. This allows for very little variation, but your skin may be much colder, even as low as 60°F.

Your body produces at least 90 kilocalories of heat in an hour, and three to six times this amount during hard work. The larger

[1] *Man in a Cold Environment* by A. C. Burton and O. G. Edholm, Arnold, London, 1955. See also *Climate and the energy of nations* by Markham, Oxford University Press, 1944.

part of it is produced in the muscles. On an average, you must
lose heat to your surroundings at exactly the same rate. Suppose
you are keeping still, and are generating 90 kilocalories per hour
within your skin. If less than 90 kilocalories per hour escape
across your skin, your body becomes warmer: if more, it becomes
colder. Fortunately your body has a high heat capacity, its
specific heat being 0·83 of that of water. If you weigh 10 stones
your body's heat capacity is close to 53 kilocalories per deg. C,
and if one tenth of your bodily heat fails to escape, you will rise in
temperature by only 0·17°C in an hour.

The task of keeping warm in cold surroundings is therefore
that of allowing only 90 kilocalories per hour, if you are keeping
still, to escape through the skin. It is simply necessary to enclose
the body in clothing which has just the right overall resistance to
heat flow, or thermal insulation. Thermal insulation can be measured in terms of the inverse of the heat flow (kilocalories per
hour) across one square metre of the material, when its two surfaces differ in temperature by one degree Celsius. This unit,
however, is rather abstruse for ordinary people, and another unit
with a much shorter name, and magnitude 0·18 of the above, is
sometimes used instead. This is the clo unit, and it may be
visualized as the amount of thermal insulation that will keep you
indefinitely comfortable in a sitting position in a room at about
21°C (70°F). Your metabolism is supposed to be 50 kilocalories
per square metre per hour, and the air in the room is supposed
to be of less than 50 per cent relative humidity, slowly moving
round at 20 ft/minute. To English people one clo would be provided by lightish summer clothing.

The clo unit can be used for measuring the thermal insulation
both of clothing and of the body tissues. Let us be logical and
first apply it to the body, where the heat originates. In normal
activity such as walking or swimming, the insulation of the body
is equivalent to only about 0·2 clo. It would be much greater if
the body merely conducted heat like a solid, but in fact the circulation of the blood has the effect of rapidly transporting heat to
all parts, just like the hot water pipes in a centrally heated house.
However, the body can cut off the blood supply to the parts
nearest the skin, by a muscular constriction of the blood vessels
just under the skin. This process is called vasoconstriction, and it
happens whenever the skin gets unduly cold. In conditions of

vasoconstriction, for instance when the body is in a cold bath, by reason of reduced circulation under the skin, the body's insulation rises to nearly 0·5 clo. An extra 0·5 clo may be added if the body is exceptionally fat, averaging say one cm thickness of fat under the skin instead of the more usual 3 to 4 mm.

Another mechanism besides vasoconstriction which safeguards against too much loss of heat is shivering. This is an uncontrolled muscular activity near the skin which generates heat, up to three times the normal heat production of the body at rest. Unfortunately shivering requires plenty of blood circulation, so the blood vessels are reopened. It is not possible to get the benefit of vasoconstriction and shivering at the same time.

The next obstacle to the escape of heat is the clothes, and these may have an insulation of 0 clo (for no clothes) to 6 clo (for a thick Arctic suit). Outside the clothes there is still a layer of air which remains more or less attached to them and is sometimes called the boundary layer. Air is a very good insulator and this layer has the effect of 0·8 clo in still weather, falling to 0·2 clo in a wind.

Other heat is lost from the body by breathing-in cold dry air and breathing-out warm humid air. The evaporation of moisture within the respiratory tract requires quite a lot of heat, and the total effect of breathing is usually to lose 10 to 15 per cent of the body's basic heat production. There are also some heat losses in excreta but these are unimportant.

Evidently in cold conditions a very great deal depends on having the right clothing. Over the proper choice of clothing, there is a simple but effective rule: the thermal insulation of clothing is proportional to the thickness of dead air enclosed. In fact the entire insulating effect of clothes is due to the air trapped in them. String vests act on this principle, by ensuring that a good thickness of air is trapped under the shirt. Unfortunately it is also important to prevent the circulation of the trapped air, so that it will not work to dress ourselves in a sort of rubber balloon and blow it up harder every time we want to increase the insulation.

The insulating value of dead air (i.e. of air which cannot circulate) has been found to be 4·7 clo per inch. Garments an inch thick, quilted and stuffed with kapok or a similar light fibrous material, given an insulation of 4·7 clo. An Arctic suit of this thickness would have to leave much of the face clear, and the hands if they

were to be any use could only have relatively light insulation, so
the whole outfit might have a value of only 4 clo. It is generally
considered that $1\frac{1}{2}$ inches of clothing is the greatest thickness
a man can wear without his mobility being seriously impaired, and
that therefore 6 clo is the maximum of insulation that can be
given to a mobile man.

Two other considerations besides dead air content are important in the design of clothing for cold conditions. The first is
penetration by wind. A penetrating wind of 24 miles per hour can
reduce the insulation of standard clothing by 1·5 clo, so the outer
fabric of cold clothing must be made as wind proof as possible,
and the seals must be effective at neck, wrists and ankles. Incidentally, the movements of the man inside his clothes usually
displaces the dead air so much that its insulating power is
appreciably reduced, but this is not altogether a bad thing, since
a moving man generates more heat anyway. The second important
consideration is moisture. By far the quickest way of moving heat
from A to B is by the evaporation of water at A, moving the
vapour and condensing it at B. When the clothing is dry, the heat
lost by the skin through the evaporation of sweat and insensible
water is given back to the clothing where it is absorbed by the
fibres. This can go on for an entire day without any appreciable
escape of heat to the outside air and afterwards the clothing can
be redried ready for use again. Wool has the ability to take up
more moisture than most other fibres without losing its springiness
or its power to entrain dead air.

At this stage, it is fair to ask whether there is really a difference
between wet cold and dry cold. Certainly in our climate there are
many days when the air is cold and humid, and it feels much
colder than the temperature indicated by a thermometer. This
happens most often when the temperature is near freezing, and
the damp air penetrates our clothing and seriously reduces its
insulating power. It can never happen at temperatures below
about $-5°C$ or $23°F$, because even saturated air will then contain
a quite trivial amount of water vapour. Any excess water would
have to be in the form of snow, and this luckily does not penetrate clothing.

A final point before actually choosing which Arctic suit to wear
for the day: if you are adequately protected against cold for a
sitting down job out of doors, you will turn unbearably hot should

you decide to run about. You will need to remove several layers before you do so, and not all of these suits are removable a layer at a time.

We can also learn something from human races who have been resisting cold without the help of science, for many generations. Physiologists have found that the bodies of Australian Aborigines, Kalahari bushmen and the natives of Tierra del Fuego are all specially adapted to survive cold. So are the Eskimos with their rich fatty diet, and it is dangerous simply to go and live like them, though some of their methods are very sound indeed. They wear double fur clothes and their igloos are superheated. When they come in from long periods of exposure they undress and the heat rapidly soaks into the layer of fat that has been protecting the inner organs of their body. This is the ideal way of recuperating from intense exposure to cold.

The most effective method of wearing fur clothes is that of the People of the Little Hills, described by the present-day Canadian writer, Farley Mowat. These Eskimos of inland Arctic Canada dress entirely in caribou skins. The outer garments have the fur outside but the inner trousers and parka have the hairs on the inside, all bending downwards. During exercise the perspiration evaporates from the skin, condenses on the hair of the parka and runs off over the outside of the trousers. In this way no heat is needed to redry the garments. Until recently these people had no access to seal blubber or other high-grade fuels, but had to rely on twigs grubbed up from under the snow. Besides being hard to find, such twigs produce fires which are too smoky to be tolerated in the airless interior of an igloo. Therefore the inland Eskimos, by all accounts a happy, unworried people, used to live for long periods in winter without any fires at all except an occasional small fire of twigs for cooking.

We can learn even more from the long distance swimmers, in spite of the relatively high temperature of the water in which they swim. Immersion in water is astonishingly chilling as every bather knows, because heat is so easily transferred from our body to the water in contact with it and from there to more distant water. Standing dry but unclothed in air of the same temperature as the water, we cool down much more slowly, particularly if there is little wind blowing.

Medical experts writing in the *Lancet* have said that Channel swimming is possibly the greatest feat of endurance in the world of sport. What is the advice of Dr H. Baddeley, Medical Adviser to the British Long Distance Swimming Association? If we are likely to be severely exposed to cold, we should first go in for special training, involving increasing periods of immersion in cold water. We must learn not only to resist cold but to avoid overheating when we come out—at first our body reacts too slowly and we sweat profusely when towelling ourselves dry. Our diet should contain plenty of fat and protein, and vitamin C, thiamine, riboflavine and vitamin B12 are all helpful during training. We should aim to build up a uniform thick layer of fat under our skin.

Dr Baddeley has two special and rather surprising tips. Learn not to be afraid of cold: psychic disturbance, as he calls it, is dangerous. Secondly, if your hands and feet are always getting cold, wear a really warm hat: the body loses nearly half its heat from the head, face and neck. And grow a beard for the same reason.

Here are some important temperatures for swimmers.

Water at 60°F: a non-acclimatized but fit young serviceman will survive only 3-6 hours. Major Zirganos, who was considered to be the greatest marathon swimmer of all time, could live indefinitely in water at this temperature.

Water at 59°F: limb muscles begin to lose power.

Water at 55°F: Dorothy Perkins, of Bradford, swam the English Channel when the sea was at this temperature, and crossed it in just under 20 hours. This is about the limit of what a fully trained swimmer can do.

Water at 53°F: at this temperature the body has no power to protect the inner organs, however hard the muscles are worked. Surface blood vessels open out instead of staying constricted, and cold blood flows into the inner parts of the body. Major Zirganos suddenly collapsed and died while swimming the Irish channel, and is believed to have been swimming at the time in a patch of water at this temperature.

Metal objects at 30°F: must not be touched with the bare skin. The moisture and tissue beneath the skin quickly freezes with disastrous results.

Bad conductors of heat at −40°F: quite safe to touch for limited periods.

Air at —60°*F:* harmless if you are properly dressed and prepared for it.

Water at 40°*F:* one hour's immersion need not be fatal if the right treatment is given. No food or drink of any kind, but one method is sudden immersion in excessively hot water at 122°F. An alternative is very gradual warming in air at 65°F. Intermediate rates of warming up have been found to be dangerous.

Apart from physical collapse, the main dangers out of doors in cold weather are trench foot and its severe form, frostbite. In the Korean war of 1950–51 25 per cent of all American casualties in the winter were due to cold injuries, mainly frostbite. The advice given to British soldiers is to use the Buddy system—go out in twos. One person helps another, who may begin to show the symptoms of frostbite such as whitened hand, nose or feet, and will help him to get up if he falls. Keeping moving, and exercising the fingers and toes, helps to fight off symptoms. The greatest single danger to watch for is extreme pain in a finger, toe or limb. If this pain suddenly stops, while the sufferer is still exposed to cold, it is imperative to move him to shelter and warmth at once.

Survival in the cold is evidently a task for the professional, and its techniques are still being evolved by such bodies as the Medical Research Council. Anyone who exposes himself and risks the exposure of others through bravado deserves scorn rather than praise. Cold must be faced in deadly seriousness.

Chapter Four

TEMPERATURE

ONE ADVANTAGE of the caloric model was its seemingly simple explanation of the flow of heat. Bodies in contact shared out their caloric until there was no reason for it to flow either way. Similarly the caloric within any body, however complex, even containing gaseous or liquid enclosures, distributed itself throughout until no further tendency to flow remained.

In modern terms, without going into mathematics, we cannot do much better. We can say that bodies in contact share their combined heat energy in proportion to their heat capacities, or that they reach thermal equilibrium with each other. This is an entirely experimental conclusion which has never yet been proved wrong, so we accept it. Some scientists think it is comparable in importance with the First Law, and they even call it the Zeroth Law, on the analogy that zero comes before one. (There are now four laws of thermodynamics, numbered 0, 1, 2 and 3!)

The importance of the Zeroth Law is that it explains why we can make and use thermometers, and construct scales of temperature. Suppose we have any sort of thermometer, and a thermos flask containing warm water. Every time we dip the thermometer in, it must share the heat of the water in the same way, or else its reading of temperature would be different and the whole exercise would be nonsense. If now we put the thermometer into another flask of water and it reads the same, the two samples of water must be at the same temperature—mixing them together would not alter the temperature of either. All these statements are consequences of the Zeroth Law, and if they were not true we should not be able to measure temperature or to use thermometers reproducibly.

Thermometers were first made three hundred years ago, two hundred years before the scientists had realized that heat was different from temperature. The two were so hopelessly confused for such a long time that it is better to forget about history and make a fresh start. Let us begin with two facts.

(1) Heat is a form of energy. Although it is often measured by using thermometers, it can if necessary be directly measured in the ordinary units of energy.

(2) Temperature is a very particular property of bodies which changes when heat flows into or out of them. It can be measured only with thermometers.

The Gas Thermometer

With this knowledge let us design a thermometer. The first step is to make a search for measurable properties of objects which change systematically when heat flows into or out of them. This search will yield a formidable list, from which we may well leave out such clumsy devices as the solubility of salts and the voltage of cells. At least ten are in current use for accurate temperature measurements, and seven of these are listed in the table.

Some temperature-dependent properties

the length of a rod
the volume of a vessel
the volume of a quantity of liquid
the pressure of a gas kept in a fixed volume
the resistance of a wire (increases as temperature rises)
the resistance of a semi-conductor (decreases as temperature rises)
the brightness of a lamp filament (high temperature only)

We should probably choose the third of the above properties if we wanted a *convenient* thermometer, and the result would be a typical mercury-in-glass thermometer such as can be bought from instrument makers and laboratory outfitters. Instead, we shall choose the fourth property, the pressure of a gas. The resulting thermometer will have a tremendous range, and give readings at all temperatures between that of liquid helium and that of melting sulphur. It will also be *absolute*, i.e. the readings will be independent of the gas we put in. Finally, it will be accurate to about 0·1°C. The main difficulty will be that a single reading may require several days' hard work in the laboratory for dealing with technical problems such as the dead space correction because some of the gas is in the glass stem at a different temperature, gas absorption and temperature equilibrium, and for applying numerous corrections. A lot of time will be spent also on preparing the specimens whose temperatures are to be measured. These are

almost invariably pure substances at their melting or boiling point.
When their temperatures are accurately known, they will be used
for calibration of more convenient thermometers such as the

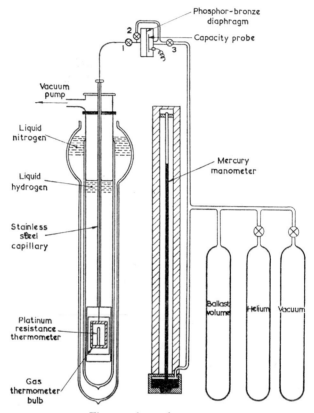

Fig. 4.1. A gas thermometer.

platinum wire resistance thermometer, and these in turn will be
used in research.

One of the numerous corrections arises because the gas thermometer reading is not independent of the gas put in unless its
pressure is low enough, so low that accurate readings are difficult,
and would interfere with the dead space correction. The difficulty

is dealt with by making a separate study of the gas to be used in the thermometer, observing with great accuracy its changes of volume under different pressures. This gas can then be used in the thermometer at pressures which are convenient to measure, and corrections can be applied afterwards.

Temperature Scale

There are only eight laboratories in the world where temperature is measured absolutely, to such high accuracy. There is one each in Australia, Canada, England, France, Germany, Japan, Russia and the United States. Over the years these laboratories have found out what an absolute thermometer will read at a whole series of natural fixed temperatures, which they call fixed points. The major fixed points are listed in the table.

Fixed points of the international temperature scale

Boiling point of oxygen	−182·970°C	90·18°K
Melting point of ice	0	273·15
Boiling point of water	100	373·15
Boiling point of sulphur	444·600	717·75
Freezing point of silver	960·8	1233·95
Freezing point of gold	1063·0	1336·15

These six temperatures are enough to ensure that all measurements involving temperature, anywhere between −240°C and 2000°C are accurately reproducible.

As it happens, there is one kind of thermometer which reproduces its readings even better than a gas thermometer. It is the platinum resistance thermometer, using the fifth of the temperature-dependent properties listed in the earlier table. Unfortunately it is not an absolute thermometer, because no two pieces of platinum wire can be made exactly alike—in contrast with gases, all of which have identical temperature dependence if their pressures are low enough. However, all the best platinum resistance thermometers agree with each other to very small fractions of a degree. For convenience, therefore, the fixed points have been defined to an extra place of decimals, beyond what can be reproduced with a gas thermometer.

Two columns of figures are given in the table. The left hand column records temperatures in the centigrade scale (this has recently been renamed the Celsius scale after a Swedish professor of astronomy in the period 1730–44). The right hand column is the Kelvin scale, named after Lord Kelvin, a Glasgow professor of physics. Lord Kelvin was an almost exact contemporary of Queen Victoria, and an expert on many sciences from submarine

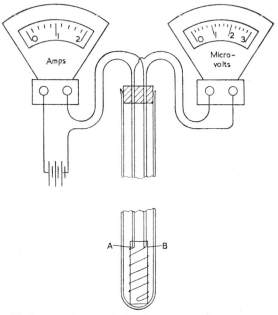

Fig. 4.9. Platinum resistance thermometer designed to measure the resistance of the spiral platinum wire between A and B. The microvolts have to be read to 7 figures and the amps to 6 places of decimals – and this is not possible with dial-reading instruments.

cable laying to thermodynamics. Notice that every temperature in °K is exactly 273·15 more than the corresponding figure in °C. The reason for this will appear in the next section but one.

With the help of fixed points, scientists can calibrate any thermometer, made of any material, to give a correct reading even at temperatures which are in between the fixed points. If a high quality mercury thermometer were properly graduated to read without correction between 0°C and 100°C, the graduations would not be exactly equal. Those near 0°C would be slightly further apart than those near 100°C, but you would need exceptionally good eyesight to notice the difference!

Fahrenheit and Some Earlier Scales

D. G. Fahrenheit, a modest German instrument maker who spent most of his time in Holland and England, bequeathed the well known scale which is so much used in Britain, America and elsewhere. Perhaps it is at last on the way out, because in 1963 the Meteorological Office began to give temperatures in °C, with equivalents sometimes in °F. Weather men used to like the Fahrenheit degree, because it was small enough to avoid the need for decimals for some purposes. Doctors like it too, because the body temperature of 98·4°F is so near to 100 (actually Fahrenheit thought the body temperature of a healthy man was only 96°F).

The measurement of temperature was for a long time chaotic, there being so many different scales in use. A textbook of 1785, called *A System of Mechanics* by Rev. T. Parkinson, M.A., Fellow of Christ's College, Cambridge, has a plate showing the following scales of temperature: Fahrenheit, Florence (two scales), Paris, D. la Hire, Amontons, Poleni, D. Reaumur, D. l'Isle, Crucquius, Royal Society, Newton, Fowler, Hales and Edinburgh.

Here are some of the observations quoted in Parkinson's book. (Note. His definition of *temperature* is "the heat or coldness in bodies, whether within the limits of perception or not". Evidently he uses "heat" and "temperature" as synonyms, and logicians will see that the definition is a circular one.)

Fahrenheit
- 106° Heat of the skin in an Ague-fever
- 97° Heat of a hive of bees
- 96° In water of this heat a Perch died in three minutes
- 48° Temperate air in England and Holland
- 32° Water just freezing or Ice and Snow just thawing
- 0° A mixture of Snow and Salt, which freezes Oil of Tartar, per deliquium, but not Brandy
- −39° Mercury freezes

Newton
- 192° Heat of burning Coals in a small Fire made of bituminous Pit-coal and not blown with the bellows
- 136° Heat with which burning bodies shine in a dark night but not at all in the twilight
- 96° The least heat by which Lead melts
- 34° Heat with which Water boils vehemently
- 12° Heat of the thermometer in contact with the human Body and of a Bird hatching her egg
- 0° Water begins to freeze

Absolute Zero

Whenever its temperature rises by 1°C the constant-volume gas thermometer undergoes a set rise in pressure. This set rise is, as accurately as can be measured, 1/273·15 of the pressure in the thermometer when it is at 0°C. Suppose, as in Fig. 4.1, a column of mercury similar to a barometer is used to measure the pressure in the gas thermometer; and suppose when the bulb is in melting ice the pressure is 100 cm of mercury. Then, at a temperature of 273·15°C the pressure will be 200 cm of mercury, and at 546·3°C it will be 300 cm of mercury and so on. But what happens at −273·15°C? Only an ideal gas would remain a gas at this temperature, but scientists assert quite definitely that its pressure would be zero!

If we try to imagine a gas whose pressure is zero we have to think of the situation when all its molecules have stopped moving; none of them collide, or try to escape. They have no energy and it is impossible to cool them further by taking energy from them. In fact, no gas theremometer can be cooled below −273·15°C. For over 100 years this fact has been known, and the temperature of −273·15°C is called absolute zero. When the Absolute scale of temperature (now known as the Kelvin scale) was introduced, 273·15 was added to every temperature on the centigrade (Celsius) scale, and 0°K is therefore another way of writing absolute zero.

Although no gas thermometer like the one in Fig. 4.1 has ever been cooled to absolute zero, very simple ones have been cooled below 1°K. Can other things than gases be cooled any further? Certain crystalline salts, with a small amount of helium condensed on their surface, have been cooled below 0·01°K. Their temperatures could only be estimated from certain magnetic properties of the salts. They, too, had very little atomic or molecular energy left, and there was no evidence at all that they might ever be cooled below 0°K.

Absolute zero, then, is the ultimate "depth of cold". It is the absolute limit of low temperature, though there is no known limit to the amount of heat that can be put into a material, and experiments have been carried out with ionized gases at millions of degrees (Celsius or Kelvin). For some reason, many people find low temperatures rather frightening, but they ought to be far more frightened of the sort of high temperatures that are now reached in industry and in the laboratory. Even at red heat (600–700°C), a poker is more dangerous than one at about −270°C. The effect of touching a very cold object, as a matter of fact, is rather like touching a very hot one. The pain is the same as the pain of burning, and the tissue damage is similar and has to be treated in the same way. Cold liquids, too, are relatively harmless to the skin. Liquid air at −190°C can be spilt over the hand with less harm than an equal amount of boiling water at 100°C.

There are other dangers however, only indirectly due to the low temperature. If a sealed vessel containing any cold liquid is allowed to get warm, above what is called the critical temperature, the entire liquid turns to gas. For liquid air the critical temperature is −147°C, so the accident can easily happen. The gas will build up a pressure approaching 1,000 atmospheres, if the vessel is strong enough. If not, the vessel will burst, and the explosion will probably be violent enough to endanger life and wreak havoc in the room where it occurs.

Even worse explosions, and fires too, can occur when the liquefied gas is oxygen. Pure oxygen gas, as is well known, supports combustion five times as rapidly as ordinary air. If liquid oxygen is spilt from a vessel and runs over the floor, as it evaporates it quickly supplies oxygen to any flame or spark in the vicinity. An ordinary fire will become unmanageable for even cast-iron firebars will burn in oxygen. Other liquids with high fire risk are hydrogen and methane, for the obvious reason that if they boil the gases are extremely combustible.

Chapter Five

SNOW, ICE AND THE ICE AGES

ON MANY DAYS of the year anyone, in any part of the world, can look out of the window and see ice. Even on a hot summer day, the air in the stratosphere 40,000 ft up has a temperature of −50°C to −60°C. The troposphere for quite a depth below this will also be well below zero. If there are any clouds in this region, and there usually are, we would expect them to be clouds of ice crystals rather than of water droplets. These are what we must look at if we want to see ice.

The photographs show some types of clouds which are high enough to be in this cold part of the atmosphere, and to be composed of ice crystals. They show an aircraft condensation trail or contrail with a little cirrostratus in one corner, and cirrus, like mares' tales, all above 20,000 ft and cooler than −25°C; altostratus and altocumulus, at 7,000 to 20,000 ft and 0°C to −25°C; and the thunderstorm cloud cumulonimbus, the anvil-shaped top of which may reach 40,000 ft and be as cold as −50°C.

Apart from their fascinating beauty, clouds have the attraction of being difficult to understand properly—so much so that there is a Professor of Cloud Physics in the University of London, for example. All the natural clouds shown in the photographs can only exist where there is a widespread region of ascending air, and of course the air must contain a lot of water vapour. In these circumstances, all sorts of things happen, such as:
(1) the air cools as it ascends, because the pressure diminishes, but (2) cooling causes water to condense within the rising air, forming ice particles; however (3) the heat of condensation is absorbed by the air so that it is not as cold as the air outside the cloud, so (4) the cloudy air goes on ascending. Moreover (5) the ice particles naturally tend to fall and (6) while falling against the upward current of the air they tend to grow by attracting more water vapour molecules to them, although (7) they may break up into smaller particles which are carried upward by the rising air. (8) Those particles which grow big enough to fall out of the

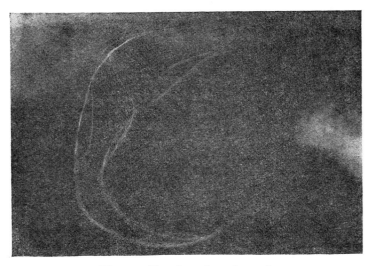

Fig. 5.1. Aircraft condensation trails.

Fig. 5.2. Cirrus.

Fig. 5.3. Altocumulus against a background of altostratus.

Fig. 5.4. Cumulonimbus.

bottom of the cloud may not fall to the ground as snow or rain, and most of them do not, because they usually evaporate into the unsaturated air below the cloud. (9) In cumulonimbus clouds, the lower regions consist of water droplets and hailstones. The entire cloud is a vast electrostatic machine in which electric charges are separated in a field of about 1,000 million volts—but thunderstorms are not our concern in this book. (10) The particles or drops within a cloud contain only a small fraction of the available water molecules: all the remainder are in the form of water vapour. Any particular molecule is liable to play a succession of rôles in the cloud, changing from vapour to ice, to water, and back again to vapour.

Thus a cloud is anything but the rather inert looking object we see sailing majestically across the sky. It is a complete laboratory of physical happenings. Besides all this, clouds play an enormous part in the atmosphere as a whole. For instance, they concentrate the tremendous energy of hurricanes, and they release energy to provide most of the ordinary wind. They help to keep the earth at a fairly even temperature, reflecting away much of the hot sunshine by day and retaining the earth's heat by night.

Ice Crystals

The amount of water vapour needed to saturate a given volume of air diminishes very markedly as the temperature is reduced. Thus an ascending mass of air, not saturated with water vapour to start with, will soon reach a level and a temperature at which the water vapour already in it is enough to saturate it. Above this level, water vapour ought to condense, forming ice if the temperature is below $0°C$ and water if it is above.

This is what in fact happens if ice particles or water droplets are present already (having fallen from a still higher level perhaps). The water vapour condenses on the existing particles, making them bigger so that they fall faster. But if there are no particles present, and the air is perfectly free from all solid impurities, the water vapour will not condense until a level is reached where it is seven-fold supersaturated. We know this only from laboratory experiments because ordinary air is never absolutely pure. It always contains some particles, called condensation nuclei, on which water vapour will condense when there is only moderate supersaturation.

In our case, we are concerned mainly with ice particles in the cloud types shown in the photographs. Careful experiments have demonstrated that although ice particles are all crystalline they can have at least three different shapes. If the air becomes saturated at 0°C to -3°C the ice forms in hexagonal plates, at -3°C to -5°C in needles, and at -5°C to -8°C in hollow columns. At lower temperatures still the patterns recur with variations. Snow-flakes which have grown gradually within a cloud of varying temperature can thus have a mixture of crystalline forms and this contributes much towards their great beauty.

Snow, Rain and Hail

Meteorologists use the word precipitation to describe what falls from clouds, irrespective of whether it is water or any form of ice or snow. Precipitation occurs when some of the particles in a cloud reach such a size that they fall in spite of the upcurrents which sustain the clouds. In spite of Galileo's famous experiment in which he showed that large and small cannon balls take the same time to fall from a height, rain and hail particles fall at speeds which depend very much on their size. This is because they are small, and they fall far enough to reach an equilibrium speed at which the drag of the air on them just equals the pull of the earth, i.e. their weight. Typical cloud drops are so small that in still air they would fall at only 1 cm per second. A typical raindrop falls at 6 metres per second. Hailstones the size of golf balls, which do occur although they are luckily quite rare, fall at 30 metres per second—over 60 miles an hour.

Whatever form the precipitation takes as it leaves the cloud, it is most likely to reach the ground unchanged if it descends quickly. Light raindrops and snowflakes may never reach the ground at all because of the long time they have in which to evaporate. Sometimes they can be seen as "rods" or "virgae" hanging below the level bottom of clouds in the middle distance. Normal snow flakes descend rather slowly in any case, and if the air is above 0°C they will usually melt and reach the ground as rain. Sleet mostly occurs when the air is only a few degrees above 0°C and the snow has not had time to melt fully.

Hail, because it falls so fast, can occur at all times of year. Almost always it comes from the cumulonimbus cloud, where particles can grow big while supported by the strong upcurrents.

The International Cloud Atlas recognizes eight kinds of precipitation. Besides rain, drizzle, snow and hail it describes snow pellets (formerly called soft hail), snow grains, ice pellets and ice prisms. Snow pellets are white opaque grains of ice with a diameter of 2 to 5 mm which are easily crushed. Snow grains are the same, but smaller. Ice pellets are up to 5 mm in diameter, but they are hard and transparent or translucent. Ice prisms are commonest in polar regions; they are unbranched crystals and so small that they hardly seem to be falling; when they glitter in the sunshine they are easiest to see.

Radiation and its Reflection by Snow

In Chapter Four the Zeroth Law apparently depended on the ability of heat energy to "flow" by conduction. A still more useful way of moving heat is to warm some water and move the water—this is called forced convection. Natural convection occurs when differences in density cause air or water to circulate. In one sense, however, the most important of all way of transferring heat energy is by radiation—because without radiation from the sun, the earth would not be warm enough to support life at all.

Radiation of heat is no different from the radiation of light. Of the energy in a sunbeam, over half is in visible light and the remainder mostly in infra-red (dark) radiation, of too long a wavelength to be visible. Compared with the sun, the earth is a weak but efficient radiator of heat, in very long wavelengths far in the infra-red. In general, energy is radiated from all objects at a rate proportional to the fourth power of the absolute temperature. Using $6,000°K$ for the temperature of the sun, and $300°K$ for that of the earth, this means that the sun is $6,000^4/300^4 = 20^4 = 160,000$ times as strong a radiator, per unit area of surface, as the earth. Nevertheless the radiation from the earth's surface and the back radiation from the atmosphere are extremely important in determining the temperatures in which we live. The temperatures of the ground, the sea and the air are all such that there is a balance between the heat coming in (by radiation from the sun) and the heat going out (mainly through radiation from the earth and atmosphere into outer space), but the details of the balance are complicated because of many secondary sources of radiation, such as clouds.

Radiation is rather like the hare in Mrs Beaton's cookery book—

you first have to catch it. The catching or absorption of radiation is only one of the three things that can happen to it when it encounters matter. It may alternatively be reflected in the way that clouds and snow reflect most of the sunlight that falls on them, or it may be transmitted in the way that water and glass transmit light. We can observe for ourselves how long fresh snow will survive in strong sunshine, because it absorbs so little of the radiation. People often sunbathe in the snow and are quite warm because their skin absorbs radiation easily, while the snow actually helps by reflecting extra radiation on to them. Dirty snow melts more easily than clean snow because of the radiation absorbed by the dirt. Notice how footprints melt before the fresh snow around them. Ice, too, is a fairly good absorber of radiation.

Glaciers are often defined as ice masses on the surface of the earth which survive from year to year, and are moving. There are a few snow-filled corries in Scotland which often survive through the summer, but these are not glaciers. It is a near thing, though, because there would be glaciers in Scotland if the mountains rose to 5,000 ft, only 600 ft higher than Ben Nevis.

Any true glacier has a survival problem: enough snow must fall on it in winter to make up for the ice that melts and runs away in summer and for the direct evaporation of ice. This balance between accumulation and ablation determines whether the glacier is growing or shrinking. In recent years the Alpine glaciers have receded quite a lot, but this is by no means a sure sign that the climate is dependably getting warmer.

Research is going on in the hope of explaining how the snow which year by year falls on the top of the glaciers is transformed into ice. Although it is true that the snow flake is an arrangement of ice crystals, the ice deep down in a glacier is of different form—sometimes it contains single crystals weighing several pounds. The air trapped by the snow flakes has to be largely pushed out somehow, and the molecules of water have to migrate to new positions. No doubt in many glaciers the process is helped by partial melting and refreezing, but it goes on too in dry polar glaciers which never melt at all.

All glaciers move, the fastest grinding their way downhill at a rate of tens of feet per year. The movement of glaciers was once thought to be caused by the melting of the lower ice under the weight of the ice above, but this is a fallacy. In many cases the pressure is insufficient to melt the ice, and even when it is sufficient, the water stays between the crystals and plays little part in the flow. What happens is a phenomenon called "creep", which is the slow deformation of any crystalline substance under stress. Creep goes on in solids at any temperature, but naturally is most obvious near the melting point. Metallurgists have made very careful studies of the creep of engineering metals. They have to guard against such eventualities as the failure of turbine blades after too short a life at their operating temperature. The creep of glaciers is not of such vital importance, but it is being studied, and surely it is well named!

The Ice Ages

The world is apparently emerging from an ice age which was at its most intense about a million years ago, and the emergence is very gradual with frequent set-backs. A million years is not a very long time by geological standards. There were other ice ages much earlier—one over 200 million years ago when the coal fields were formed, and one over 500 million years ago.

In the last ice age, during its most recent period of severe glaciation, the whole of Europe north of the Alps must have had a miserable climate. It was a region of tundra vegetation, inhabited by reindeer, woolly rhinoceros and mammoth. Around the Mediterranean sea there was plenty of wind and rain, and a climate like that of present day France or England. Where the Sahara desert now is, was a genial land in which early forms of stone age man were beginning to flourish.

Until as recently as 8300 B.C. a vast ice sheet covered Finland and Scandinavia. At one time there had been 13 million square miles of permanent ice in the world, nearly 7 per cent of its whole surface. It was mainly in Antarctica and North America, with over a million square miles each in Europe and Asia, and smaller ice sheets in Australia, New Zealand and South America. In many places the ice was thousands of feet thick: so much water had gone to make it that the sea level was 300 ft lower than it is now. We still have 6 million square miles of ice in Antarctica and Greenland. What catastrophic flooding there would be round every coast if these were all to melt! It has been estimated that the sea would rise by 130 ft, in

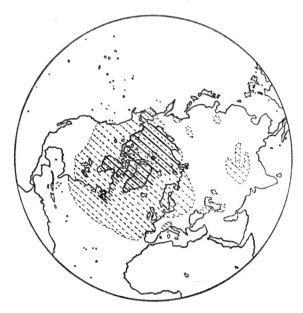

Fig. 5.5. North Polar ice today, and at its greatest extent.

which case most seaports, including London, would be largely submerged.

From the time when the ice sheet began to recede, the climate of Europe became drier and warmer. Then it became moister but warmer still, until about 4000 B.C. when it was about 5°F warmer than it is now. Since then, irrespective of variations from one year to the next, there have been many long-term fluctuations lasting a century or more. We are now a degree or so warmer than the average and 4°F warmer than the worst cold period in historical times, which lasted from 400 B.C. to 100 B.C. The warmest centuries in the English historical period were A.D. 800–1200. The Norse voyages of this period to Iceland, Greenland and America appear to have been made in ice-free conditions, and Viking ships or their equivalent would find the journeys much more difficult today. In A.D. 1600 the European glaciers all began to advance, and they did not start to recede again until 1850.

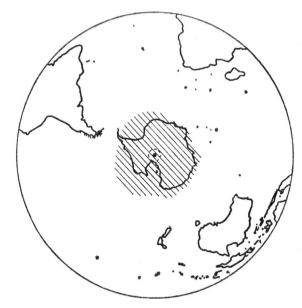

Fig. 5.6. South Polar ice today.

North Polar Ice

The mass of ice which floats on much of the Arctic ocean, and which persists through every summer, is a major feature of our north European climate. Winds from the far north in summer are much colder than wind which has not passed over this ice.

The extent of the ice cap may be measured in degrees of latitude, between the North pole and a representative position on the very irregular southern edge of the ice. In summer it reaches from the pole to the 78th parallel, an angle of 12°, in distance about 800 miles. This "permanent" ice is very thick and old. In winter practically the whole ocean north of the Arctic Circle, which is $23\frac{1}{2}$° from the pole, is covered by floating ice. The Russians have difficulty in keeping their Arctic sea routes open even in summer. The Canadians do not even find it worth while to try, any further than Hudson's Bay.

The permanent ice within 12° of the pole seems to be quite impregnable, but it could be destroyed during a long series of warm summers if there happened to be frequent gales. The sea underneath it, reinforced by relatively warm water circulating up from the depths, would break it up at the edges, and the resulting icebergs would drift off and melt away. In fact there probably was no persistent ice in much of the period between A.D. 500 and 1000. Although the water froze round the pole each winter, the ice was often not thick enough to withstand the combined onslaught of sun and storms during the summer.

C. E. P. Brooks, in his book *Climate through the Ages*, has pointed out that the difference between failure and success in the formation of permanent ice is very small. The freezing point of sea water is about 28°F or −2·2°C. If over an open polar ocean the winter temperature falls only to about 27·4°F or −2·6°C, an ice cap will develop which will extend rapidly until it reaches a latitude of about 78°. From then it will grow more slowly to about 65°. The ultimate lowering of the winter temperature brought about by the initial small fall of 0·6°F, will amount to about 45°F. The drawing shows how Brooks represents the winter temperatures between the North pole (latitude 90°), and 50° which is about the latitude of Cornwall and Newfoundland. The curve labelled "Glacial" is a fair representation of temperatures experienced on the Atlantic and Arctic oceans in a typical present-day winter. The upper curve, "Non-glacial", is what would be experienced in the absence of an ice cap. This may well be what was happening when the Vikings penetrated to America, and it can be seen that northern Iceland would then be climatically rather similar to north Scotland of today.

Yes, the word "glacial" used just now in association with winters of the present day is simply an alternative for "ice age". We must face the fact that we are living in an ice age, still. After all, the Quaternary glaciation, which is the one we are mainly talking about, began only a million years ago, and a million years is a very small part of geological time.

There seem to have been four great glaciations regularly spaced during the last 750 million years. Each one has lasted not more than a few tens of millions of years. The much longer intervals between them, over 200 million years each time, have been warm and humid in most parts of the world. In these unimaginably long warm periods, appreciably more of the earth's surface than now was covered by sea, and the land was mainly flat and swampy.

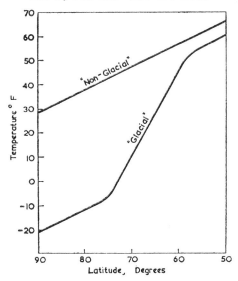

Fig. 5.7. Winter temperatures in the northern hemisphere; now, and as they might be.

Let us reflect that our present climate obviously suits us very well, for we have developed spectacularly compared with all the other animals of the Quaternary era. In fact, we like living in our ice age, though we probably hope it is not going to turn any more glacial in the near future.

Cause of the Ice Ages

Many different explanations have been offered of the tremendous changes in climate between the normal warm periods and the relatively short ice ages between them. There have been astronomical explanations, such as variations in the emissive power of the sun, and the passage of the solar system through clouds of interstellar dust which would absorb some of the sun's radiation. Other astronomical suggestions are changes in the ellipticity of the earth's orbit, and changes in the inclination of the earth's axis. Geographical explanations include the change in position of the world's land masses, affecting ocean currents and air circulation. From within the earth, causes have been considered like variations in earth heat (radioactive, biological or volcanic), and the effects of volcanic dust and water vapour. The carbon dioxide in the air has been thought hard about, because it strongly absorbs part of the earth's radiation, and conserves the earth's heat in the same way as a glass roof conserves the heat in a greenhouse. All these are important ideas, but the explanation which best fits the facts, as we know them now, is that the ice ages are primarily caused by mountain building, which is caused in turn by the development of large scale weaknesses in the earth's crust.

Each great period of mountain building has had an ice age associated with it. The last two, at least, of the glaciations began after the main upheaval of land had occurred, when the first wide round topped mountains had worn into more jagged shapes, like the Alps and Himalayas that we know. This lag has been explained as due to the time needed for cooling the warm oceans and to the tendency of mountain tops to rise slowly higher as their sides erode away.

An increase in the mountainous areas of the world has a whole series of consequences on the weather. First, since it is well known that clouds tend to form on mountains, the total cloudiness of the world must increase. Now clouds obviously reflect sunlight well, for they appear brilliantly white when lit by sunshine. Hence, the additional clouds must reflect still more of the sun's energy back into space instead of allowing it to warm up the earth. This produces rather colder weather in which the average temperature might be lower by as much as $1°F$.

Second, it is also rather obvious that mountains are often covered with snow. This reflects radiation even more than cloud, and the winds spread its coldness to surrounding areas of land and sea. The effect of extra snow altogether might amount to a fall of $3°F$ over the world as a whole.

Third comes the well known heavy rainfall or snowfall in mountain regions. All this precipitation must be balanced by extra evaporation of water, mainly from the sea. Evaporation, as we have previously seen, uses considerable heat energy which in this case can only come from the sea and cause a lowering of its temperature. The effect of evaporation attributable ultimately to mountain building can be estimated as a general cooling of $4°F$.

There are other indirect consequences of mountain building, nearly all of which produce a general cooling. Winter by winter, we must imagine, the polar air and the ocean beneath it cool from the mid-thirties towards the freezing point of 28°F. Patches of ice appear in the polar seas in some winters and melt away again in the summer. After many centuries, perhaps, a succession of cold seasons occurs in which the average is below 27·4°F. The ice spreads very much during each of the winters and does not melt away entirely in summer. The polar ice now begins to affect climate in a big way, right down to temperate latitudes. Instead of long periods of settled weather over the plains and oceans, the routes and frequency of the low pressure areas are largely controlled by an anticyclone which persists over the pole. Neither the warm winds from the equator nor the even more important warm ocean currents can penetrate into the polar regions, and the ice age really begins.

These conjectures of Brooks and other climatologists are at present the best explanation we have of the four great ice ages, each of which was associated with a great period of great mountain building. Since the average duration of an ice age is ten million years we must not suppose that anything happens suddenly. The cooling of the ocean must take a great deal of time, and the ocean deeps probably continue to get colder for many thousands of years after the ice caps and other glaciation have formed. On the other hand, the climatic change itself, in which sultry, settled weather gives way to the so-called polar front, with its strings of depressions, bright periods, gales and outlooks unsettled, might occur relatively quickly, in less than a thousand years, perhaps.

Which way will the world's climate change in the next few hundred years? The climatologists are still a long way from knowing the answer. Their problem has a superficial similarity to that of the daily and monthly weather forecaster, but, as we have seen, it is really very different. All that can be said at present is that, as far as anyone knows, the climate is equally likely to turn warmer or colder.

Chapter Six

METHODS OF COOLING

IT IS ALL VERY WELL to cool an over-hot bath by adding cold water, or to cool any hot body by touching it with a cold one, but this method is no use when the temperature required is lower than that of any available natural substance. This is the requirement of most modern low temperature research, and of many technological applications: to reduce the temperature of objects which are already cold. Fortunately there are several ways of doing just this, though they are much less straightforward than the converse problem of putting heat into objects which are already hot. The most important methods of reducing temperatures use (1) freezing mixtures, (2) removing the vapour, (3) internal work and (4) external work. For achieving the lowest temperatures of all there is only one good way (5) demagnetization.

(1) **Freezing Mixtures**

Freezing mixtures depend on the availability of ice or snow. Pure ice melts and water freezes at o°C, but if about an equal weight of salt is added, the melting point is much lower. A freezing mixture is made by simply mixing common salt or some similar chemical with granulated ice. A little ice melts immediately, but melting requires quite a lot of heat energy, sometimes called the latent heat of fusion. The heat to melt each gramme of ice comes from the still unmelted ice nearby, for example, through cooling about 70 grammes of this ice from o°C to −1°C. The salty water percolates among the granulated ice, more of which melts, abstracting more heat energy from nearby ice and water. Finally the mixture consists of very cold salt solution in which the last granules of ice are melting. The same amount of heat energy is in it as at the beginning, assuming that none has flowed in from the surroundings, but the water molecules have lost their orderly crystalline arrangement and have acquired freedom of movement. The energy which caused simple vibration of atoms in the crystal has been shared among the water molecules to give them energy of rotation and translation too. This means that less energy is available for the bulb of any thermometer immersed in the freezing mixture, and the temperature is therefore lower.

Temperatures of $-20°C$ can be reached by mixtures of ice and common salt. With calcium chloride or zinc chloride, $-50°C$ can be achieved.

(2) Removing the Vapour

Freezing mixtures employ the trick of mixing salt and ice to make a material supply its heat of fusion from within itself. Removing the vapour is a way of making a liquid supply its heat of boiling or vaporization from within itself. It is an application of what might be called the washing line effect.

If you can find a line of washing, and touch it or wrap some of the cloth round a thermometer bulb while it is still fairly wet, you will find it is several degrees colder than the air around you. This is because the water in the cloth is steadily escaping by evaporating, and the heat energy needed to remove each molecule of water must be drawn partly at least from the cloth. The latent heat of vaporization of water is about seven times the latent heat of fusion of ice, so we have here a powerful means of cooling.

Nevertheless there is a limiting temperature below which the clothes on a washing line cannot be cooled. It depends on the temperature of the air and the proportion of water vapour it contains. On the other hand, there is theoretically no limit to the cooling obtainable if the moisture is made to evaporate into a vacuum, with the help of a vacuum pump. Imagine first a sealed glass vessel containing water, with nothing above the water except water vapour, all air having been previously removed from the vessel. Molecules near the surface of the water will be all the time escaping into the vapour space, and obtaining the energy to do this by cooling the liquid. However an equal number of vapour molecules will be returning to the water, and giving an equal amount of energy back to the water. In this way the system stays in equilibrium, and the temperatures of both the liquid and vapour are unchanging.

Pumping the vapour. Now arrange to remove the vapour molecules as soon as they escape from the water, by attaching a pump to the vessel. The water level will slowly go down of course, but the water remaining will get colder and colder. It is fairly easy to cool water from room temperature to its freezing point, and to make ice, using the apparatus shown in the figure. Incidentally, as the bubbles in the water show, it is really boiling.

Water is not a good liquid for the experiment, because of its high capacity for heat (its specific heat is 1 calorie per gramme deg. C); also because of its peculiar changes in density which rather inhibit natural mixing (it becomes *less* dense when cooled from 4°C to 0°C, and ice is less dense still). A more suitable material is liquid nitrogen, whose specific heat is only 0·43 calories per gramme deg. C. With modern facilities there is no problem in handling this very cold liquid, which boils in an open vessel at −196°C, or 77·5°K. The apparatus in the figure

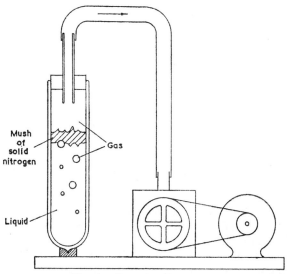

Fig. 6.1. Pumping the vapour.

will rapidly cool liquid nitrogen from this temperature to its solidification point 63·4°K when the pump is switched on, and solidify it completely in a few minutes more. A reasonably powerful pump, moreover, will continue to pump vapour quite fast from the solid nitrogen, thereby cooling it another five degrees or more. Ultimately, the rate of evaporation of molecules from the excessively cold solid becomes so small that further cooling is prevented by heat leakages into the system.

Blowing off the vapour. There is no difference in the physical laws of a gas kept below atmospheric pressure by a vacuum pump, and a gas compressed by a compression pump until its pressure is above atmospheric. After all, the pressure of the atmosphere is due to the weight of an envelope of gas around a particular planet. If a gas is compressed it gets warmer, because the molecules hitting the piston of the pump bounce off with increased velocity. But if this heat is taken away somehow, and the gas is kept, say, at room temperature, at a high enough pressure it may liquefy. Examples of gases which can be liquefied like this at room temperature are ammonia, sulphur dioxide and freon. Now suppose some liquid freon, the least poisonous of the three, is obtained in a sealed steel vessel, and then the vessel is opened to the atmosphere. The freon vapour will first rush out until the pressure falls to atmospheric, followed by more vapour from the boiling liquid. Just as in the pumping-the-vapour experiment, the heat of vaporization must be taken from the liquid left behind, and we end up with a steel vessel partly full of liquid freon, gently boiling at its normal boiling point, $-28°C$. From the physical point of view this method of cooling is identical with pumping-the-vapour, but experimentally it is more messy and more dangerous.

(3) Internal Work by a Gas

The method of compression and boiling has rather a chequered history, and as will be seen in the next chapter it failed to surmount the last obstacle, leaving three gases still unliquefied. These three were all first liquefied by the method of internal work, which might be looked on as a sort of latent heat. The latent heats of evaporation of liquids, and of fusion of solids, are well known. In simple molecular language, they represent the energy needed to separate molecules, either from the loosely bound state in a liquid, or from the regular crystal lattice of a solid. Both melting and boiling require energy because internal work is being done, the work of separating molecules from each other when they "want" to cling together. We might wonder, then, whether internal work is done in separating the molecules of a compressed gas if it is allowed to expand, and whether here, too, some kind of a latent heat is involved. At first sight, the idea seems not very hopeful, because we would still need evidence that the molecules of a compressed gas likewise tend to cling together. However, such evidence is in existence in refined measurements of certain physical properties of gases. Gases are in fact found to be doing internal work when they expand, and as a result they cool a little, but there is one important proviso. Each gas must be below a certain temperature, which depends on the pressure and is not in any case particularly far above the normal boiling point of the substance. At higher temperatures than this the gas will get warmer instead of cooler as it expands.

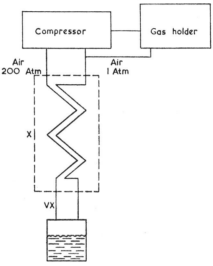

Fig. 6.2. Cooling by expansion through an orifice at VX.

The whole question of internal energy of gases was studied in the 1850s and 1860s by Joule and William Thomson, who was later raised to the peerage as Lord Kelvin. The changes of temperature are called the Joule-Thomson effect. The temperature for a particular gas at a particular pressure, above which there is heating and below which there is cooling on expansion, is called the Joule-Thomson inversion temperature. To reproduce the Joule-Thomson cooling it is necessary to compress the gas to the right pressure and bring it down to the right temperature. There is no need for the gas to do any external work as it expands, such as by driving the piston of an engine: expansion through an orifice will suffice, into a long tube or other closed vessel attached to a pump.

Although Joule-Thomson cooling is only a small effect it is ideal for the liquefaction of gases, because it requires no mechanical parts such as pistons and valves in the cold region. Such parts might generate heat by friction, and might even seize up. The small cooling effect can be built up into a large one by making the gas recirculate and cool itself regeneratively, as in the sketch. Here the gas is compressed, cooled to room temperature in a water cooler, and then further cooled by some of itself which has just expanded at the orifice. Thus every new unit of gas has the advantage of being pre-cooled by previous units. After an interval during which the whole apparatus cools down, drops of liquid begin to form at the expansion orifice, and drip into the reservoir below.

(4) External Work by a Gas

The drawing represents an important experiment which is worth thinking about but not worth doing, because very large errors can easily creep in. The pump barrel is 16 in. long and 1 sq. in. in sectional area. There are 15 one-pound weights on the pan and they together exert a force equal to the atmospheric pressure, so when first put on they compressed the air in the barrel from a 16 in. to an 8 in. column. There was a temporary increase in temperature, but let us suppose that the compressed air inside is now back at room temperature. What happens to its temperature if a single one-pound weight is removed? The compressed air has to push the other 14 weights upwards, together with a column of air weighing 15 lb. In spite of these forces it pushes all the weights upwards through a distance which can be calculated to be 0·25 in. It therefore has to do work amounting to 29 × 0·25 inch-

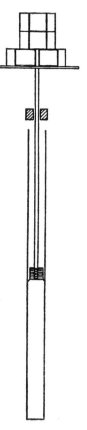

Fig. 6.3. External work by a gas.

pounds, which is 0·63 foot-pound. The energy needed to perform this work is 8·4 million ergs; it has to come from the heat energy of the air which therefore diminishes by 0·2 calorie. The mass of air in the pump barrel is 0·27 grammes, and the removal of 0·2 calorie of heat lowers its temperature by 3°C. Calculations show that if the other weights are taken off one by one the air temperature will be lowered by 54°C!

How did the necessary energy come from the heat energy of the compressed air? Energy was transferred every time the piston was moving upwards, because molecules of air colliding with it bounced back with less energy than if it had been stationary. (It is true that half the molecules of ordinary air colliding with the weights above the piston were bouncing back with extra energy, but we are concerned with the temperature of the air inside.)

So it is possible to cool a gas by making it do external work. A single stroke of the piston does not cool it very much: although the air alone might cool by 100°C or more, it has to cool the much heavier metal parts at the same time. However, by going through many cycles of compression with heat exchange followed by expansion, a great deal of heat can be removed from the gas and from material in contact with it. Expansion engines are now used in research laboratories all over the world, for liquefying helium and producing the lowest temperatures of all. The problem of operating pistons and valves without sticking or generating friction at these low temperatures was solved in 1934 by Dr P. Kapitza of Cambridge, England. The design was developed and made commercial by Dr S. C. Collins, an engineer at the Massachusetts Institute of Technology.

(5) Cooling by Demagnetization

The mention of cycles and engines brings us very near to the Second Law of Thermodynamics. This can be expressed in a number of equivalent ways, but it has the effect of stating, for example, that you cannot sail a liner across the Atlantic simply by utilizing some of the enormous heat energy in the water beneath you. In a more practical form the Second Law states that the work done by an expansion engine gets greater as the temperature of the cold parts gets further and further below the temperature at which heat exchange takes place during compression. The work done is equal to the temperature difference divided by the temperature, in °K, of the cold parts. If the engine has inefficiencies due to friction or temperature inequalities it has of course to do still more work.

In yet another form, the Second Law states that if disorderly atoms and molecules are rearranged in a more orderly manner, energy is needed. When a material is magnetized, parts of its atoms which are sometimes called the magnetic ions are turned until they all face the same way. The arrangement is thus more orderly than before, and heat energy has been used. How can this fact be turned into another method of cooling?

The method was first made effective in Leyden, Holland. A crystal of magnetic salt, iron-ammonium alum, was put in a strong magnetic field. Its magnetic ions were thereby all turned the same way, and the work done on them reappeared as heat energy in all the atoms of the crystal, i.e. the crystal became warmer. So next the crystal was cooled to its former temperature by ordinary means. Now the magnetic field was switched off, allowing the magnetic ions to return to their original disorder. In doing so they removed energy from the non-magnetic atoms of the crystal, which became cooler in consequence.

Demagnetization works best at very low temperatures where the relatively small change in energy of the magnetic ions is comparable with the total heat energy in the non-magnetic atoms. In the first successful experiments, the starting temperature of the iron-ammonium alum was only $1 \cdot 25°K$. When the magnetic field was switched off the temperature fell to $0 \cdot 017°K$! Since then, experimentalists have obtained temperatures well below $0 \cdot 001°K$.

The best materials for cooling by demagnetization are crystals in which the magnetic ions are well separated by ordinary non-magnetic atoms. It might be thought that a material containing many more magnetic ions would give a better result. Unfortunately the ions influence each other too much if they are close together, as in pure iron, with the result that when the field is switched off they continue all to face in the same direction; and no cooling occurs.

So far we have looked at the five main methods of cooling in a rather academic light. When human flesh and blood enter the picture it naturally becomes much more lively, especially when it contains a blend of nationalism and scientific pride. There was a most exciting race towards absolute zero, spread out over more than fifty years. In its own way it was comparable with other challenges, like the race to the North and South poles and the assault on Everest. Its story will be told in the next chapter.

Chapter Seven

INTO THE DEPTHS

AT THE BEGINNING of the nineteenth century there were many gases which had never been seen in the liquid state, and scientists were eager to produce them, and to see what sort of liquids they were. Everything that was then possible had been done by simply cooling the numerous gases and hoping they would condense into liquids. Michael Faraday in 1823 had the idea of compressing them as well. After all, every liquid was much denser than the corresponding gas, so a combination of cooling and compression might do the trick.

Faraday made small amounts of various gases and sealed them in glass tubes of his own design, as in Fig. 7.1. He strongly

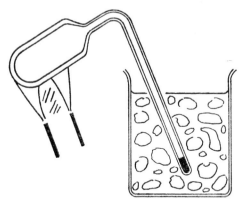

Fig. 7.1. Faraday's method.

heated the wide end of the tube, and thereby increased the pressure of the gas everywhere in the tube. At the same time he cooled the remote, narrow part of the tube in a freezing mixture. The technique succeeded in two cases, and Faraday produced liquid chlorine and carbon dioxide for the first time in his simple apparatus. If he had then opened the tube and let the vapour

blow off, the liquid would have become colder still, but it is unlikely that the drop of two or liquid he had made would cool very
much before it was all vaporized.

At this stage there was more interest in liquefaction than in
cold. The very moderate compression used by Faraday had
shown that liquids could be produced by compression. With
larger scale production of gases, and the compression pumps and
hydraulic presses which were now technically realizable, perhaps
quite large quantities of liquefied gases could be made, and the
new liquids be added to the chemists' stock of reagents. Or was
it wrong to expect that all gases could be liquefied by compression, irrespective of their temperature?

Critical Temperature and Pressure

This last question proved to be crucial. How ought anyone to
set about ansering it? Surely it would be a good idea to examine
some substance that was liquid at room temperature and see
whether its vapour could still be liquefied at higher temperatures.
A French engineer, Cagniard de la Tour, tried heating a sealed
glass tube partly filled with a variety of liquids including ether,
carbon disulphide, and water. The remainder of the space in the
vessel was occupied by the liquid's own vapour; the pressure in
both the liquid and the gas increased rapidly as they were heated,
as more and more of the liquid was converted to gas. In spite of
the risk of bursting the vessel, he went on heating it until, quite
suddenly, the sharp line dividing the liquid from the gas above it
disappeared! On cooling down again a line reappeared. At one
temperature there was only gas in the tube, but immediately
below this temperature the liquid was there, with a definite
meniscus distinguishing it from the gas above. Cagniard de la
Tour measured the temperature at which each liquid disappeared:
it was 197°C for ether, 273°C for carbon disulphide and 374°C
for water. We now know that the corresponding pressures were
36, 73 and 218 atmospheres—most dangerous, unless the glass
tubes were of very small diameter. (Nowadays, industrial and
medical gases are kept in steel cylinders at 120 atmospheres
pressure.) The Cagniard de la Tour temperature and pressure
are always the same for any given substance; they are usually
called its critical temperature and pressure.

The Irish physical chemist Thomas Andrews studied these

critical phenomena with accurate measurements of pressure, temperature and denisty. What he found out applied not only to carbon dioxide, which he had chosen for study, but to every substance which could be liquefied. It must also apply to the "permanent" gases, and it explained why they should not be liquefied at room temperature.

The drawing (Fig. 7.2) represents all possible pressures and temperatures in relation to some pure substance, it does not matter which. To any temperature and any pressure corresponds

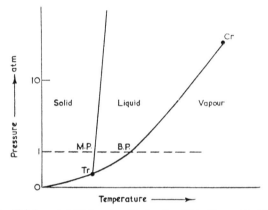

Fig. 7.2. Triple point (Tr) and critical point (Cr). Normal boiling point (BP) and melting point (MP).

one point on the drawing, and according to which zone the point is in, the substance at that temperature and pressure will be solid, liquid or gas. The two lines O–Tr–Cr and the straight line from Tr are very important, because it is easy to get the substance on to these lines. When on the straight line from Tr, the substance is a partly melted solid, and when on the curved line it is a partly vaporized liquid (or solid). At the point Tr, known as the triple point, it is the only temperature and pressure at which all three phases of a substance, solid liquid and gas, can exist together in equilibrium. The temperature 0·01°C which was mentioned earlier in connection with temperature scales is the triple point temperature of water, water vapour and ice.

Cagniard de la Tour had liquid and gaseous ether in a sealed glass tube. His substance was somewhere on the curved line between Tr and Cr. As he warmed it up it approached Cr, which is known as the "critical point". The instant he warmed it beyond Cr the meniscus disappeared and there was no longer any liquid in the tube. The work of Andrews, published in 1863, was an important advance on Fig. 7.2 because he measured the temperature and pressure of a substance, and also its *density*, at many points on this diagram. His results can be expressed in the form of Fig. 7.3, which shows how the volume of a substance is

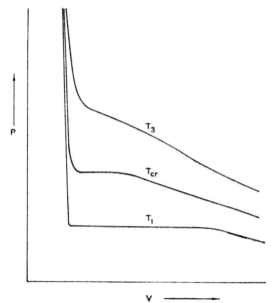

Fig. 7.3. Pressure/volume curves of a real gas and liquid.

affected by varying its pressure, while its temperature is kept constant. Each curve in the figure corresponds to a particular temperature. The quantity or mass of the substance was not changed throughout the measurements, so that the volume it occupied was inversely proportional to its density.

If the substance had behaved like an ideal gas throughout Andrews' experiments, he would have produced a somewhat different figure, Fig. 7.4. This represents the famous composite "law" of Boyle, Charles and Gay-Lussac which is approximately obeyed by gases when they are well away from the temperatures

and pressures at which they liquefy. In 1873 a great Dutch
physicist, van der Waals, found a theoretical explanation which
qualitatively accounted for Andrews' results. Moreover, for all
the substances which could then be liquefied, the "non-perman-
ent" gases, he produced an equation which fairly well foretold the
critical temperature and pressure from measurements that could
be made while they were still very much in the gaseous state. In
fact these predictions could be made within a few degrees by

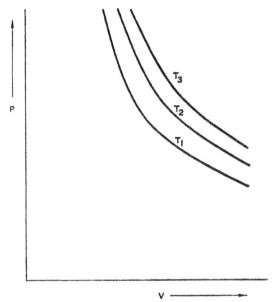

Fig. 7.4. Pressure/volume curves of an ideal gas.

measuring quite small departures from the ideal gas law of Fig.
7.4, at fifty or a hundred degrees above the critical temperature.
As more and more measurements came in, the critical temperature and pressure were predicted for all the remaining permanent
gases, nitrogen, oxygen, hydrogen and so on. Scientists then
knew, for each of these gases, what temperature to cool it to
before they could liquefy it by compression.

Now comes one of history's practical jokes, because this was
not the way in which the first of the remaining gases was liquefied.

The gas was oxygen, whose critical temperature is −118°C. In December 1877, two physicists, working independently near Paris and Geneva, liquefied oxygen by a crude method in which they compressed and cooled the gas to only about −100°C and then let it expand rapidly through a valve into the open air. A jet of liquid oxygen shot out, but immediately evaporated into a cloud of ice-cold "steam" (whenever a jet of very cold fluid blows into ordinary room air, the water vapour and carbon dioxide in the air condense and give the appearance, but not the temperature, of steam from a kettle). Liquid oxygen had, therefore, been produced, not under pressure, but by method 4, for the compressed gas had done "external" work in producing the jet of fast moving oxygen. Of course the droplets of liquid had been lost before any useful measurements could be made on them.

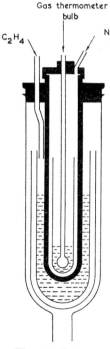

Fig. 7.5. Cracow apparatus.

In the next ten years a Polish-Austrian low-temperature research team in Cracow studied most of the "permanent" gases by first-class experimental techniques. They obtained each gas in turn as a liquid, boiling quietly in a test tube screened from room air by the cold vapour of the liquid itself.

The Cracow physicists stored liquid ethylene in a steel vessel at the fairly high pressure of 32 atmospheres, but it had to be kept at a temperature well below its critical temperature of 10°C. For this cold store they used method 1 of Chapter Six, ice and salt. By drawing off some of the liquid ethylene into an open vessel at one atmospheric pressure they immediately achieved −104°C, the normal boiling point of ethylene. They in fact decompressed the vapour by letting it blow off, method 2. By then attaching a pump to the outlet of the open vessel they further cooled the liquid ethylene by method 2 to about −150°C. The calculations of van der Waals in Holland had shown that this is below the critical temperature of all gases except hydrogen, neon and helium. By cooling such gases in a pressure vessel immersed in very cold ethylene, and by compressing them with a hydraulic press the Cracow workers liquefied them (see Fig. 7.5). Their pressure vessel was of thick glass, very carefully annealed, and they could see the liquids they made. They allowed most of the liquid ethylene to be pumped away as vapour to get it out of the way of the next stage of cooling, and then they released the pressure over the liquid oxygen or nitrogen so that this rapidly cooled to its own normal boiling point. Measurements of temperature, density, colour, magnetic susceptibility and so on could then be made. (Liquid oxygen, by the way, is blue, of the hue and purity to be seen in the clear sky after a storm.)

By pumping liquid oxygen and nitrogen, temperatures down to about $-210°C$ or $63°K$ can be reached. At this point the race towards absolute zero met an awkward obstacle, and the runners spent several years in finding a way round it. The obstacle was one of those facts of nature that we have to live with: no substance exists which has a critical temperature above $63°K$ and a boiling point below it.

There are only three substances which are gases at $63°K$. These are the elements helium, hydrogen and neon, and their critical temperatures are $5·25°K$, $33·25°K$ and $44·5°K$ respectively. Thus the brute force method of cooling one of these gases to $63°K$ or thereabouts, and compressing it in the hope that it will liquefy, is bound to fail.

The choice lay between method 3 (internal work and the Joule-Thomson effect) and method 4 (external work). Method 3 produces only a slight cooling but the gas can be pumped round and round a circuit, in which the gas is compressed, cooled by liquid air, cooled by gas which has already expanded through a valve, then allowed to expand through the same valve, returning, through a heat exchanger where it cools the next lot of gas, back to the gasholder and the compressor (see Fig. 6.2). Method 4 can be used in the same "regenerative" way, but it requires an engine to be driven by the compressed gas, at a very low temperature. The engines of those days all required oil to lubricate them —but oil turns to a hard wax at low temperatures and the engine jams up completely. Without oil it would produce so much heat by friction that all cooling effect would be lost.

An alternative way of using method 4 is to compress as much gas as possible into a pressure vessel, cool it as far as possible, and then allow it to expand rapidly into a gasholder (see Fig. 7.6). As more and more gas is pushed out of the cold pressure vessel, more and more external work has to be done by the gas remaining behind. The residual gas cools throughout the expansion, and if it liquefies the expansion just stops. Although this single expansion is equivalent to an engine which makes only one stroke of the piston, it can be very effective on a small scale if the equipment is carefully designed. The physicists of the late nineteenth century tried it often, but they produced at best only a few drops of ephemeral liquid. Their chief mistake was a failure to insulate the pressure vessel with a high vacuum before starting the expansion.

Hydrogen was the first of the three remaining gases to be liquefied, by James Dewar, the popular Scottish professor of the Royal Institution in London. He used method 3, taking advantage of the experience of Professor Linde at Munich, who developed a way of liquefying air on an industrial scale. Linde had found that the expansion valve for method 3 had to be opened only very slightly, and that this small crack became readily blocked up by solid particles if any impurity such as carbon dioxide, water vapour or oil vapour was left in the air to be liquefied. Dewar therefore carefully removed the last traces of these impurities from his hydrogen, and also any traces of nitrogen and oxygen since these, too, would have solidified and blocked the expansion valve. He produced liquid hydrogen in 1898, and demonstrated to the members of the Royal Institution that this was easily the lightest liquid known, having a density one-fourteenth of that of water.

Liquid Helium

In spite of Dewar's success with hydrogen by method 3 the cryogenic laboratories in Cracow, Leyden and London persisted with method 4 in their attempts to liquefy helium. We must remember that helium is a very rare gas, and that it had been first found on earth only recently, in 1895, though it had been detected in the sun's outer envelope in the 1860s. Such supplies of helium as the laboratories could obtain would be small, and very impure, and difficult to use with method 3. Besides, method 4, even if it failed to produce liquid, allowed some properties of this interesting new substance to be studied. Moreover, record low temperatures were undoubtedly being reached, though the methods of estimating were crude. (Once the Cracow school calculated that they had reached 1·7°K without liquefying their helium—but in fact helium liquefies at about 4·2°K.)

The honour of liquefying the last gas of all went to Kamerlingh Onnes, Professor of Physics at Leyden University. He

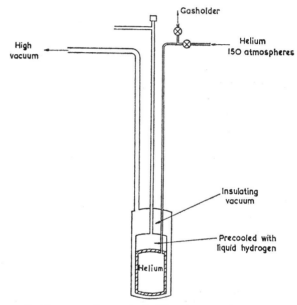

Fig. 7.6. Sudden expansion method of liquefying helium; unsuccessful in 1906, but much used in the 1930s.

measured the van der Waals coefficients for helium to very low temperatures and proved that if helium was compressed to 100 atmospheres and cooled to 14°K in contact with solid hydrogen, it should produce some liquid on a sudden expansion by method 4. At his first attempt a dense grey cloud appeared, but this turned out to be due to a very small amount of hydrogen that was mixed with the helium gas. He later produced a faint wisp of what might have been liquid helium, but regarded this phenomenon as encouraging rather than conclusive. It also showed him that his stock of helium was now very pure indeed, and was suitable for the application of method 3. He therefore built a liquefier in which helium gas was to be circulated through a Joule-Thomson expansion valve, being cooled on the way first by liquid air, then by liquid hydrogen at 15°K and finally by the returning expanded helium. There was a simple helium gas thermometer with its bulb underneath the expansion valve, read by a manometer outside.

The experiment was made in July 1908. For a very long time the circulation went on without any measurable change, but at last the temperature began to fall. It then fell more rapidly, until just as the last reserve supply of liquid hydrogen was being used it became steady, at less than 5°K. No liquid could be seen, but the steadiness was as if the thermometer was dipping in a liquid. It turned out that the liquid was there all right, but it was very difficult to see becasue of its low refractive index. What one actually observes is a line or meniscus, marking the top level of the liquid, with helium gas above it. But since the refractive index of the liquid was so near to that of the gas, the change of light in the neighbourhood of the meniscus was very slight. To make matters worse, this had to be observed through seven thicknesses of glass, one of liquid air, and one of liquid hydrogen.

The boiling point of helium under atmospheric pressure was found to be 4·2°K. By pumping the vapour, method 2, it could be made to boil at significantly lower temperatures. Fairly small pumps reached 1·0°K, though the helium has an annoying habit of boiling away unduly fast. With very large pumps the lowest temperature ever reached was 0·71°K in 1932. It was not until the 1950s that still lower temperatures were reached with an isotope of helium that was collected in small amounts from nuclear reactors.

Solid Helium

Kamerlingh Onnes' achievement may as well be regarded as the end of the race, though it was only the beginning of a succession of really remarkable discoveries which we shall come to in Chapters Eleven to Fifteen. Everyone expected, of course, that if solid helium could be produced it would have a melting point even lower than 4·2°K and present us with another useful fixed point on the temperature scale. Nothing of the sort was to happen.

After fourteen years of work, mainly on the measurement of properties of liquid helium, solid helium had never been produced, and Kamerlingh Onnes wondered whether helium would remain liquid under the pressure of its saturated vapour even if it was cooled to absolute zero. However, there was still the possibility that helium would solidify under pressure. The Leyden workers cooled a fine capillary tube containing liquid helium to a little over 1°K and submitted it to a pressure of 150 atmospheres. They found the tube was blocked. By lowering the pressure slightly and raising the temperature to 4·2°K they unblocked the tube, so they concluded that it had been blocked by solid helium. In a later experiment they put liquid helium in a glass tube, with a stirrer, at 2°K and gradually raised the pressure. At a pressure of about 35 atmospheres they were unable to move the stirrer. This time, also, the helium had solidified. There was, however, nothing peculiar to see in the tube. Solid helium is perfectly transparent.

Helium is the only substance which has no triple point, a temperature at which the solid, liquid and vapour are all present at the same time. Some day a spaceman may find a planet in some solar system which consists of solid helium, but if he does, one thing is sure. The solid will be completely submerged in either a sea of liquid helium, or an atmosphere of gaseous helium deep enough to exert a pressure of at least 25 terrestrial atmospheres. There will be no place where he can stand with one foot on land, one in the sea, and his head in the atmosphere.

Chapter Eight

DOMESTIC COOLING

IN THE HOT CLIMATES of the world, man has always had to struggle for existence. Extreme heat is probably a greater hazard to man than extreme cold. After all, in an emergency it may be possible to make a fire, but it is quite impossible to make a refrigerator. However, man has survived climatic dangers for a million years, and has built up a remarkable ability to acclimatize himself. We have seen in Chapter Three what the body does to resist cold. Let us now see what defences it has against extreme heat.

For short periods its defences are fabulous. In 1775 an experiment was made in which men remained in a large dry oven for fifteen minutes at 250°F while a beefstake was cooking. Their profuse sweating, the enormous latent heat of water and the high heat capacity of their bodies saved their lives; history does not state who ate the beefsteak, but the men would be thirsty rather than hungry.

Survival over long periods is a quite different task. The body has to achieve some sort of equilibrium with its surroundings, without allowing any part of itself, and particularly the brain, to deviate far from the normal temperature of 98·6°F. Unavoidably, the body produces heat from "burning" food to provide the necessary energy for muscular work; even at rest, this chemical activity generates 90 kcal/hr, all of which has to be dissipated if the body has a hope of surviving. Apart from this initial handicap, the body has to play a strategic game with the three heat carriers, radiation, conduction and convection, sometimes avoiding them as enemies, but at other times receiving help from them as friends. Luckily the greatest heat-shifter of all, evaporation, is always a friend.

Radiation is an enemy in most circumstances. During most of the day the sun, and all the objects heated by it, such as the sand of the desert, the rocks and the air itself, are radiating heat towards any body which is cooler then themselves. Man's defence against radiation is to reflect it away, and allow as little as possible to be absorbed by his skin. The skin is a poor reflector of radiation, however. Rather oddly, the Negro's skin is even poorer than that of white men: it reflects about 18 per cent of visible radiation, against the white man's 30 to 45 per cent. But the main heat-carrying radiation is invisible, in the infra-red region, and skins of all colours are very inefficient reflectors of this. So man devises any makeshift screen he can, including the umbrella, and the flowing white cotton garments of the Arabs. If man can find surroundings which are cooler than his body, in the jungle perhaps, then radiation is his friend. He removes all clothes, and his skin radiates heat to his surroundings.

Conduction is the least important of the heat carriers in our present context. It plays a secondary part in the transfer of heat from man's organs to his skin, and also in the reverse direction if his skin is the warmer.

Convection takes place from an object (man) which is surrounded by a fluid (air). If the object is hotter then the fluid, by conduction the nearest layers of fluid become slightly warmer than the rest. As a consequence these layers expand, becoming lighter than the rest, and therefore they rise away from the surface of the object, to be replaced by fresh layers of cooler fluid. This process is continuous and a current is established in the fluid—a convection current. If on the other hand the object is colder than the fluid, a convection current starts in the opposite direction, by the fluid sinking after being in contact with the object. These are called natural convection currents, and they considerably speed up the rate of heat transfer between the object and the fluid. Stirring the fluid in any way, driving it with a fan, or letting a breeze in through a window, is called forced convection, and this is much more effective than even natural convection for speeding up heat transfer. As might be expected, man exposes his skin and encourages convection by any suitable means whenever he is over-hot and the air feels cool to his skin; but if the air feels hot to his skin he keeps still and tries to prevent convection.

Evaporation is man's greatest natural ally in hot climates. Water is continually being lost from the body via the lungs and skin. At these surfaces it changes from liquid to vapour, and the necessary heat of evaporation, which is quite large, is supplied from lung or skin tissues close by; and they are thereby cooled.

It appears that man, in his evolution, has provided himself with mechanisms which strongly increase the rate of evaporation when extra cooling is needed. They are the sweat glands of the skin. Normally, moisture diffuses slowly through the skin from its deeper layers and evaporates on reaching the free air, with the result that the skin is fairly dry. When the sweat glands take over, they flood the skin with water and secure the maximum rate of evaporation allowed by the external conditions, namely the humidity and temperature of the air, and the air movement over the skin. The latter can be improved very much by removing clothing, and by every form of forced convection.

The sweat glands can release water at rates up to 4 pints per hour, and their water supply comes from the blood. In fact the blood has to circulate through the intestinal tract to entrain water which it delivers to the sweat glands. It also circulates through the heart muscles and all other working muscles, removing excess heat in doing so.

Evidently, a man who moves from a temperate to a hot climate requires a greatly increased rate of blood circulation. This is at first achieved by stronger action of his heart, which may have to deliver blood three times as fast as previously all over the body. Later, as the man becomes acclimatized, the total volume of his blood increases, and the networks of blood vessels in his skin open up to permit a much increased blood flow. Other aspects of acclimatization include a tendency to drink much more water and to produce a less salty sweat which not only conserves the body salt but has a higher rate of evaporation.

Naturally the newcomer to the tropics or the hot deserts is prone for a time to various sicknesses which are direct results of the heat. Until he learns to drink enough, he suffers from weakness and weariness due to dehydration. The loss of salt he suffers through sweating may give him sickness and muscle cramps. Prickly heat may attack him and make him extremely uncomfortable with itching. It is caused by blockage of the sweat glands, whereupon the sweat forces its way through the skin layers. Sunburn is another hazard, which can only be prevented by restricting one's first exposures to sunshine to less than five minutes. Finally there are major disorders such as heat exhaustion and heat stroke; these are very serious indeed, and far beyond the scope of this book.

Air Conditioning

Within the last thirty years it has become technically possible
to avoid the dangers from excessive heat by immuring ourselves
in air-conditioned buildings. Some time, perhaps, there will be
space suits for terrestrial use, and we shall be able to walk about
in the hottest sunshine, protected by miniature refrigerators and
dehydrators strapped to our backs.

Present-day air conditioning equipment is far from portable.
It may occupy up to a quarter of the building it is designed to
serve. In countries outside the tropics it is usually designed both
to raise and lower the temperature of the air, as well as to raise
and lower its humidity; so that the air is right both in summer
and winter. The following description refers mainly to its operation in hot summer or tropical weather.

The air to be conditioned has to be put through four distinct
processes: circulation, cooling, drying and purifying. The process
of purifying is necessary because clean outdoor air cannot provide
the whole needs of a building without raising the cost of machinery and power to ridiculous levels. Instead, only a little fresh air
is admitted into the system and mainly stale air from within the
building is treated and recirculated. The circulation of the air is
performed by an arrangement of wide ducts leading to central
fans. Two ducts, the supply and exhaust ducts, pass into every
room with openings wide enough to ensure an air flow at head
and body level of at least 2 ft per second. Unfortunately ordinary
ducts are good conductors of sound, and all sorts of precautions
are taken, in first class installations, to "silence" them. The sound
of rushing air, for instance, is easily generated near the fans, and
is difficult to exclude from the living rooms.

People sometimes ask why it is necessary to dry the air as well
as cool it. This is not due to any property of the air, but to a
common property of water and all liquids: the more their temperature is raised, the more vapour will they produce. In Chapter
Six we considered a sealed glass vessel containing some water,
with the space above the water filled by water vapour. We then
pumped the water vapour away as fast as it formed, and the water
became colder. This time we will not connect a pump to the
vessel (Fig. 8.1), but a manometer, which measures the pressure
of the vapour and so gives a good idea of the amount of water

vapour in the space. When we warm the vessel, the pressure rises rapidly: for a rise of 20°F above room temperature, the pressure doubles, indicating that about twice as much water has gone into the vapour state. The same would have happened if the space above the water had contained air as well as water vapour, but the pressure read by the manometer would have included that of the air, and the increase in water vapour would have been less clearly

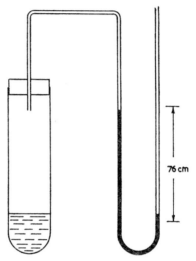

76 cm

Fig. 8.1. A liquid and its vapour.

indicated. Now therefore, in real life, in hot weather the sea, land and vegetation are all warmer than usual and they give off water vapour faster than usual. So inevitably the air will contain more water vapour than usual. This is not noticeable while the air remains hot, but if it is cooled twenty degrees or so it feels unpleasantly humid and our skins go clammy.

In a curious way the three processes, of cooling, drying and purifying the air, have merged into one another in modern plant design. The cooling, part of the purification, and very paradoxically, the drying are all accomplished by driving the air through water sprays. By circulating the spray water through the cold unit of a refrigerator (Fig. 8.2), it can be used to cool the air to any desired temperature. In practice the chosen temperature is about 55°F, because if *saturated* air at this temperature warms up to about 70°F it will have the comfortable relative humidity of 60 per cent. In the course of its journey along the ducts the air reaches approximately this condition and is therefore about right when it enters the living rooms. When the hot stale air returns to the spray chamber, as we have seen, it contains too much moisture. As the sprays cool it to 55°F some of its moisture condenses and increases the total amount of spray water so that some water escapes through an overflow. This explains the paradox of drying by means of water sprays, for the air after passing through the sprays must obviously have less water vapour in it than when it entered them. The sprays of cold water dry the air by cooling it.

Unless the air is purified before being returned along the supply ducts, there will be a steady build-up of impurities from smoke, cooking and cleaning, and eventually it will become very unpleasant to breathe. There will also be a build-up of microorganisms including dangerous bacteria. The water sprays trap some of these unwanted particles and smells. Further purification is achieved by such means as cloth filters and disinfectants. The smaller fraction of air from outdoors may also need to be purified, and may give trouble because the amount of impurity in it is not always predictable. During the great London fog of December 1952, the air filters in the air conditioning system at the Festival Hall became clogged with smoke, reducing the flow of air so much that the concert goers had to put up with a very fuggy atmosphere. Luckily the trouble could be put right by renewing the filters at frequent intervals. Anyhow, the audiences were much smaller than usual, many people having stayed at home rather than venture out into the foggy night.

Domestic Refrigerators

The one opportunity most people have of seeing a mechanical cooling system at work is the refrigerator in the kitchen. Even here, the pumping equipment and most of the pipework have to be tucked away underneath, and there is not much to see. However, one component can nearly always be seen, because it is the coldest part of the system, and is used for making ice. It is a long rectangular coil of metal pipe, inside which the water trays can be slid. This is the evaporator. It contains a liquid and its

vapour, usually freon (dichloro-difluoro-methane CCl_2F_2), and
it is cooled by method 2 of Chapter Six, pumping the vapour.

Fig. 8.2 shows how simple the works really are. Vapour
is sucked from the evaporator by the pump which compresses it
into the condenser, another coil of pipes fitted with multiple
cooling fins. The vapour in the condenser is initially hot, because

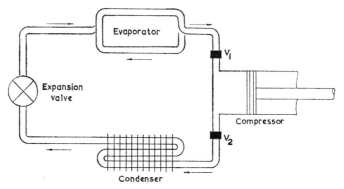

Fig. 8.2. Domestic refrigerator.

it has just been compressed, but soon its heat passes across the
thickness of the pipes, into the cooling fins, and out into the
air of the kitchen. As a result, the vapour cools enough to become
liquid at its present pressure of 15 atmospheres. The liquid runs
down the pipes to a narrow orifice, through which it is forced by
the pressure of the next batch of vapour driven in by the pump.
At the other side of the orifice, known as the expansion valve, the
liquid is below atmospheric pressure and therefore colder than its
normal boiling point, $-30°C$. It has achieved this sudden drop
in temperature by evaporating part of itself, but the vapour is
being steadily sucked away by the pump. The liquid is now back
in the evaporator, and as it evaporates it cools the ice trays, the
air and the food inside the refrigerator. Notice that the freon is
in a completely enclosed system, from which it cannot escape
unless the packing of the piston springs a leak.

It is even possible to have a refrigerator which has no pump.
This is the ammonia-hydrogen or Electrolux refrigerator. The
pressure everywhere in the system is about 15 atmospheres,
enough to liquefy ammonia at the temperature of the condenser.

The ammonia liquid runs out from the condenser into the evaporator, which contains hydrogen at the same pressure of 15 atmospheres. Here the liquid evaporates until its vapour nearly saturates the space it is in, and in evaporating it cools the ice trays in the same way as before. The vapour is collected and concentrated by dissolving it in water, and taken to a boiler where it is separated from water and returned to the condenser. The power to drive the materials round the pipe circuit is supplied by gravity and by heat from the small gas jet or electric heater which operates the boiler. (It is always possible to make a fluid circulate round a closed loop, by heating one of the vertical sections. The heated fluid expands a little, becoming less dense, and therefore it exerts a lower pressure at the bottom than does the opposite arm. The two forces do not balance, and so there is movement, which continues as long as a temperature difference is maintained. A circulating movement is also maintained in the part of the circuit containing hydrogen, because one arm holds nearly pure hydrogen which is light, while the other arm contains an addition of the heavier ammonia vapour.)

The above type of refrigerator has no moving parts and can be hermetically sealed to prevent leakages; it is also silent. It is more wasteful of energy, more thermodynamically inefficient, than the system which employs a pump. The refrigerator of the future may be different again, employing no fluid at all, unless you call electrons a fluid. If an electric current passes through the junction of two different materials, heat is either absorbed or generated, according to the direction of the current. So far, semiconductors show this effect most strongly, but not quite strongly enough for a domestic sized refrigerator to be feasible. New materials are being tried almost daily, and only a stroke of luck is needed to start another revolution in design, presenting us with "electro-thermal" refrigerators.

Modern homes seem to be full of intricate machinery, electronic, mechanical and thermal. If we had to choose which item we could least dispense with, we might well choose the refrigerator. Without it our food would have less variety and be less palatable. There would be minor tragedies through milk turning sour and fish and meat going "off". Shopping would be necessary every day, and there would be more waste, more flies and more trouble of many kinds.

Chapter Nine

COLD FOR SALE

A REFRIGERATOR is not always the cheapest or most convenient way of taking the heat out of something, or of keeping it cool. For many years there was no such thing as a domestic refrigerator, and perishable food had to be stored in ice boxes. Originally ice was kept from winter into the following summer, or brought by sea from stores in the far north. Later it was manufactured in big refrigerators. It was delivered in large slabs, and had to be broken up by servants and packed into the ice compartment of the ice box. As it melted, water dripped to the floor and was drained away. If a specially low temperature was needed, for making ice cream for example, salt was mixed with the crushed ice.

Ice is still made by specialist firms, and delivered to customers who prefer to buy their cold, rather than make it. These may include fish shops, small fishing vessels, and railway companies using ice-cooled vans for the transport of food, particularly fruit, meat and fish.

One highly scientific use of ice is for the accurate measurement of temperatures with thermocouples. A typical thermocouple, for measuring temperatures within a few hundred degrees above or below room temperature, is made of a foot or so of fine constantan wire, welded at each end to copper wires. (Constantan is an alloy of copper with nickel.) The free ends of the copper wires are connected to a potentiometer for measuring the potential difference (voltage) between them. When the difference in temperature between the two welded copper-constantan junctions is $1°C$, there is a voltage of about 40 microvolts. The relation between temperature difference and voltage can be determined accurately, once and for all, for each reel of constantan wire. Although a microvolt is small, only $1/1,500,000$ of the voltage of a torch battery, it can be measured with a good potentiometer. Thus a thermocouple can be used for measuring temperature differences to the nearest $1/40$ degree centigrade. But something else is needed if temperatures in °C, rather than merely differences, are to be measured: one of the copper-constantan junctions has to be kept at an accurately known temperature, and then the other's temperature can be determined with the potentiometer. The most easily reproduced temperature, when an accuracy of about 0·01°C is needed to be on the safe side, is that of melting ice. This is why an ice delivery van can sometimes be seen calling at science laboratories.

Things can go wrong, if care is not taken, and the temperature of the controlled junction can wander by several hundredths or even tenths of a degree. The ice merchant must be one who uses clean equipment and who never allows anything soluble to get into the water he is freezing. He must even keep out insoluble materials such as oil and paraffin. Then on arrival in the laboratory, the block of ice must be "planed" to uniform granules of about 0·1 in. in size, and the planing equipment must be kept scrupulously clean and not used for any other purpose. Finally crushed ice must be put into a small thermos flask, and distilled water be added, and the slush be well stirred with a clean wooden rod. Only then can the thermocouple junction be put in, with the certainty that its temperature will be within a hundredth of a degree of 0°C.

The ice-making plant at the merchant's factory is a large refrigerator, working usually with ammonia rather than freon. Water is frozen in big trays, and their sides have to be thawed to get the ice out. Heat for this purpose is brought from the condenser in water pipes, so that the compressed ammonia in the condenser is cooled partly by these water pipes, and partly by air blown past its cooling fins.

Indoor skating rinks have no problem of detaching the ice from its container; the container, in one form of ice rink, is a bed of frozen wet sand. The method is to lay pipes carrying brine in a few inches of sand, soak the sand in water, and freeze it by circulating the brine through a refrigerator where it is cooled to about -12°C. More water is added over the frozen sand, a thin layer at a time, and allowed to freeze until a layer of ice about 2 in. thick is formed. Underneath the sand, a thick layer of concrete is needed, supported on a four inch bed of cork, to reduce to a minimum the flow of heat from the ground beneath, and to prevent the ground from freezing.

Dry Ice

Skaters, and all winter sports enthusiasts, are no doubt properly grateful to ice, with its remarkably low coefficient of friction against a smooth surface of metal or wood. The purchasers of cold, however, are not always so pleased with it. It is not cold enough for many purposes, and it has the annoying property of being very messy when it melts. One material which overcomes these objections in a remarkable way is solid carbon dioxide, whose commercial name is "dry ice". A day's supply of dry ice is much like a delivery of ordinary ice, but it is very cold, about $-80°C$, and it disappears not by melting but by sublimation.

The diagram of state of carbon dioxide is like Fig. 7.2, but there is a remarkable difference between carbon dioxide and most other substances. The position of the triple point Tr is above the straight line denoting a pressure of 1 atmosphere, whereas for most other substances Tr is below this line. Consequently the whole liquid region of carbon dioxide is above this line, and it is impossible to have liquid carbon dioxide at atmospheric pressure. The minimum pressure at which the liquid can be kept is 5·1 atmospheres, and then it would have to be stored at a temperature of $217°K$ which is inconveniently cold. It is far preferable to store carbon dioxide as a liquid at room temperature. The diagram would show that at a temperature of $280°K$ and a pressure of 35 atmospheres, a mixture of liquid and gaseous carbon dioxide can exist. The "mixture" which is stored, in fact, nearly fills a steel cylinder with the liquid, and has a few cubic centimetres of the gas at the top. If the temperature rises by $20°$ to $300°K$, the mixture has to find a new point on the curve, namely $300°K$, 60 atm). If there is room in the cylinder at this temperature and pressure for all the carbon dioxide as liquid, and a little to spare, there will again be a few cubic centimetres of gas at the top. If there is not quite enough room, the liquid will fill the whole inside, the point representing its state will be just above the curve, and the pressure will be just above 60 atmospheres.

Carbon dioxide is kept like this, as liquid in cylinders, whenever it has to be stored for a long time. For short periods of a day or less, and when it is needed as a provider of cold, it is kept in the solid state. The point (280,1 or 300,1) in the diagram is right in the gaseous region, so there is no question of the solid being in temperature equilibrium. If a block of carbon dioxide is delivered to your laboratory, you can take off its paper wrapping and stand it on a bench. It will stay there, very cold, but evaporating and getting smaller all the time, until after several hours it has all vanished. It would have kept still longer if the wrapping had been left on, and would have survived overnight in a properly insulated container.

Manufacturers of dry ice have to begin by finding a suitable source of carbon dioxide gas. The gas is common enough. Air contains 0·03 per cent of it, and wherever coal or oil is burnt the chimney gases contain about 10 per cent of it, but the simplest processes for liquefying and solidifying it require nearly pure carbon dioxide. Fortunately it is made in large quantities in the brewing industry—when grain is fermented, carbon dioxide bubbles rise to the top of the vats and the gas soon fills the whole of the enclosed space above. Instead of escaping through small openings to the air it is collected, freed from moisture and organic materials, and compressed.

To convert it into dry ice the compressed gas is first cooled back to room temperature (compression has heated it), and it condenses into the liquid state. The liquid is passed along a pipe into a vessel one end of which is stopped by a large piston, something like a very big single cylinder engine. In this vessel, which is well insulated, the pressure of the liquid is lowered, first to 5·1 atmospheres and then to atmospheric pressure. Much of the liquid boils off and returns to a gasholder, but it takes so much heat from the rest of the liquid that this solidifies, and the vessel becomes loosely packed with fluffy carbon dioxide "snow". At this stage the piston is hydraulically driven into the vessel until the snow is compressed to dry ice at a much greater density. An end is removed and the block of dry ice is pushed right out, ready for wrapping and dispatch.

The best known use of dry ice is for keeping ice cream cool in the cold boxes of small shops and delivery tricycles. It is also used to keep cold the passengers' food in aircraft. For the transport of perishable goods by road and rail, vans refrigerated by dry ice are now being used extensively. Formerly there were difficulties because some of the food was damaged by excessive cold, but carefully designed modern vans have a separate bunker for dry ice which is able to maintain a uniform but not too low temperature in the food compartment. This type of refrigeration is particularly suitable for journeys up to about 24 hours, because only one charge of dry ice is needed. For much shorter journeys, it may be satisfactory just to precool the vans at the loading point, and to load them with food which has already been made as cold as permissible. For much longer journeys, in America and elsewhere, it may be economical to install mechanical refrigerators on the trucks or trains.

Containers for Cold Liquids

In some countries quite large quanitites of liquid nitrogen are bought by the laboratories of universities and industrial research departments. In England, there is also quite a market for liquid helium. These liquids are not only colder than the two solids which have been considered so far in this chapter; it is also their nature, as liquids, to make excellent thermal contact with the sides and bottom of any vessel containing them. Thus it is no use trying to keep a cold liquid in a single walled vessel of any kind: the liquid boils violently while dew from the atmosphere collects on the outside of the vessel and rapidly turns to layer upon layer of ice.

For holding small quantities of liquid nitrogen, helium, hydrogen or oxygen, no better device has been found than the vacuum flask of silvered glass invented by James Dewar in 1890. This is an object lesson in the prevention of heat transfer, well known to fourth and fifth formers, and it has some features of interest to physics students in universities. To get to the cold liquid by conduction in a solid, heat must travel by a long, poorly conducting path down from the top of the inner glass vessel. It would get in by convection in the air space between the two walls, but this air has been removed before the space was sealed. Not absolutely all the air can be removed, but the molecules remaining are so few that they rarely collide with each other but merely bounce across from wall to wall; their mean free path is greater than the distance across. (If anyone doubts whether the convective transfer of heat by air is important, let him try keeping liquid nitrogen in a vacuum flask whose vacuum has gone soft, through the leakage of a little air in through a faulty seal. The nitrogen boils strongly, and the outer wall feels cold and collects quantities of dew by condensation from the atmosphere.) Finally, some heat must be radiated from the warm outer wall to the cold inner wall. Even at room temperature a relatively large surface such as that of the outer wall will radiate heat fairly fast. However there is a law that, if a surface is a good reflector of light and heat radiation, it is a correspondingly bad radiator and absorber. So the inside of the outer glass envelope is coated with mirror silver, and also the outside of the inner glass vessel to make it a poor heat absorber. In manufacture, both surfaces can be easily and cheaply coated, and about 90 per cent of the heat transfer by radiation is saved.

Unfortunately, the whole weight of the interior is borne by the ring of glass which unites the two glass vessels at the top, and this is a mechanical weakness, especially if the flask is a large one. For containing a liquid of the density of nitrogen (0·8 of that of water) the largest practicable glass vessel would hold about half a gallon, and even this would be liable to break if it were tilted, for example to pour some of the liquid out. However, vessels for up to 5 gallons are in use, made on the Dewar principles, but made of metal. The spherical parts are made of copper, which can be electropolished on the radiating surfaces until it is just as poor an emitter of heat radiation as silvered glass. The inner neck is made of the poorest metallic conductor of heat, copper-nickel or german silver, and because even then it is a much better conductor than glass, it is made very long and narrow. The uniting ring at the top is strongly made of brass. The flexibility is such that the two concentric spheres can easily move with respect to each other, so they are kept in position with spacers of spongy plastic material, whose conduction of heat across the vacuum gap is quite negligible. The illustration shows such a vessel hung inside a still larger similar vessel, for the storage of liquid helium (Fig. 9.1). Liquid helium would not keep in a single vessel because of its lightness and very low heat of evaporation, but when the outer vessel is charged with liquid nitrogen it keeps very well. Notice that the outer sphere of the helium container is all at the temperature of boiling liquid nitrogen, $77^{\circ}K$; its ability to radiate is only $77^4/293^4$, i.e. 0·0048 of its value at a room temperature of $293^{\circ}K$. Notice also that the very top part of the inner helium neck is cooled by the vapour from the slowly evaporating nitrogen. The granulated charcoal in the two vacuum spaces is to improve the vacuum. Any residual gas in these spaces is strongly absorbed by the charcoal, especially when it is cold. The upper layer of charcoal is hardly likely to be necessary, though, because any residual air in this space condenses on the surface of the innermost sphere of all, whose temperature is 4·2°K when there is liquid helium inside.

To get liquid helium out of these vessels a tube with two right angle bends, shaped like a syphon, is used. The whole tube is double walled except for the lower end of the dipping arm, and

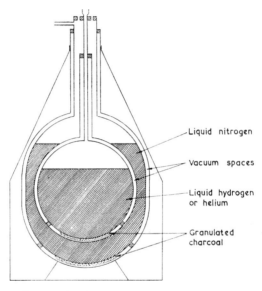

Liquid nitrogen

Vacuum spaces

Liquid hydrogen or helium

Granulated charcoal

Fig. 9.1. Double metal Dewar vessel, holding
3½ gallons of each liquid.

is made of two copper-nickel tubes with a vacuum space between. The liquid is "blown" out by admitting helium gas at the top. The complete container for liquid helium, holding 3½ gallons, costs almost £200; the transfer tube costs £30.

There is once again a limit to the practicable size of all-metal vacuum vessels, but they fail in a quite different place from the neck. The outer copper sphere has a vacuum inside it, and the pressure of the air is 15 pounds per square inch on its outside.

The force on a square foot of it is very nearly a ton so, as a rough guide, one of the copper hemispheres from which it is made must be able to support one wheel of a four-ton lorry. In practice hemispheres up to about 2 ft diameter can be made with sufficient strength, but anything larger would have to be intolerably heavy and costly. There is a well-known experiment to demonstrate how weak a strong looking vessel can be when it has a vacuum inside. Wash out a one-gallon oil can, put a little water in it and heat it until the water is boiling vigorously. Remove the flame and immediately screw on the cap. The steam inside will soon condense, and there will be little pressure inside the can to oppose the 15 lb per square inch exerted on its outside by the atmosphere. The can will crumple into a decrepit shape and be fit only for the dustbin.

Much larger double walled vessels are made for the storage and transport of cold liquids. They are mostly used for liquid oxygen just now. Recently in America large road tankers were carrying liquid hydrogen across the Nevada desert for an experimental purpose, and now, for the British Gas Board, special ships are bringing liquid methane by sea from the Mediterranean. The story will be told in a later chapter.

A typical large modern storage tank holds 100,000 gallons. The space between the double walls is filled with a powder insulant. As there is now no question of radiation from wall to wall, both shells of the vessel are made of steel. Even when the spaces between the powder granules are filled with air, the thermal insulation is moderately effective, but it is very greatly improved by removing the air, that is by pumping with a vacuum pump and sealing it tight. Inevitably, some of the liquid boils away, but the cold gas is not wasted. It is led round a long spiral embedded in the powder insulant, and is warmed on its way out by some of the heat that would otherwise have penetrated to the inner vessel. The great size of these vessels is in their favour, and the percentage losses of liquid by evaporation are very small. If we imagine them to be spheres of radius r, they will hold an amount of liquid proportional to r^3; but the rate of inflow of heat is proportional to the surface area, i.e. to r^2. Thus, for example, by doubling r the flow of heat into the container is increased fourfold, but the quantity of cold liquid is increased eightfold, so the percentage loss by evaporation is halved.

Who buys liquefied gases for the sake of their coldness ? There are no great industrial uses for cold delivered in this form. Road tankers with heavy loads of liquid oxygen can be seen on their way to steelworks, engineering works and shipyards, but it has to be reconverted to gas before it can be used. It is transported as a liquid because it is far less bulky that way than as a gas compressed in cylinders. Formerly, appreciable quantities of liquid oxygen were delivered to laboratories and used as a coolant in research, particularly where high vacuum systems were needed. But the oxygen gas escaping as this liquid evaporated was a potential danger, because it could convert an ordinary manageable flame into a raging fire. Newcomers to the laboratories were often given a striking demonstration. First a little liquid oxygen was spilled on a stone floor where it quickly produced a low lying, steamy vapour. Then a lighted cigarette was thrown down, and it burst into a brilliant flame. Another demonstration used a small piece of cotton wool, no bigger than a matchbox. A little liquid oxygen was spilt on to it and a light applied from at least 6 ft away, on the end of a rod. The cotton wool exploded with a bang that would have found favour on Guy Fawkes' night.

Laboratories now use liquid nitrogen almost exclusively, the research workers having persuaded the manufacturers of liquid oxygen to modify their equipment enabling liquid nitrogen, which they anyhow make, to be drawn off into transport tankers. A lorry with a ton or more of liquid nitrogen will drive into the back regions of a big laboratory where eight or ten five-gallon vessels stand waiting. The driver uncoils an insulated pipe, pushes it into the neck of one of the vessels and turns a valve. There is a hissing and a steaming, and in under half a minute the vessel is full. Only 10 minutes or so elapse before he is off again to his next port of call. Laboratory workers come out with two-wheeled dustbin carriers, grab the handle of a vessel with the hook of a carrier, and trundle it off to a laboratory. Here it may be placed on a tilting stand and used to fill small glass Dewar vessels, or it may have a dip pipe fitted, and a compressed air supply is admitted to drive the liquid into some machine for which it is wanted. Liquids, even very cold ones, can be transported and transferred with remarkable speed.

Not long ago, at a lecture to demonstrate some of the more spectacular properties of cold materials, some combustible materials caught fire on the bench. The air was rich in oxygen because a demonstration using liquid oxygen had just finished, and there was quite a blaze in no time at all. The assistant quickly picked up a vessel of liquid nitrogen and poured it on the flames, which died down as suddenly as they had sprung up. Liquid nitrogen is an ideal fire extinguisher if it happens to be available.

Chapter Ten

COLD IN INDUSTRY

THE ALL-IMPORTANT function of cold in heavy industry is for separation of gases from mixtures. Among the gas mixtures which are separated by cooling and liquefication are air, coke-oven gas, oil refinery gases and pure hydrogen. Chemically speaking, of course, hydrogen is a pure substance, but one atom in every 6,900 is deuterium; this has identical chemical properties with ordinary hydrogen, but it behaves very differently when bombarded by neutrons and it is needed in the production of nuclear energy. The valuable products from the separation of the other gases which were mentioned are oxygen, nitrogen, argon and rare gases from air, hydrogen from coke-oven gas, and ethylene from oil refinery gases. We shall first see what components are needed in a big gas separation plant, and then see how they can be put together.

Although the separation of gases requires a good deal of fundamental science and technology as well as engineering, one factor at least is on the side of the plant designer. His raw materials and products are all fluids, and he can therefore design a continuous flow process. Whatever we need for living nowadays we try to make by a continuous process. Cement, bricks, chemicals, wire and cables, nylon stockings, motor cars, plastic mackintoshes, sheet glass and hundreds of other necessaries are cheap, relatively to prices in the eighteenth or nineteenth century, because they are as far as possible made in this way. Henry Ford discovered how to make cars in an assembly line, which is the equivalent of a flow process, and his name will always be remembered for this, as well as for his cars. There have been some famous engineers in the business of liquefying gases, but their ideas and inventions, however brilliant, achieved only small advances beside the giant stride of Henry Ford.

The best example of a gas separation plant is one which produces useful pure gases from air. A typical plant will take in 8,000 cubic metres of air per hour, as much as fills a theatre seating

1,000 people. At one of its outlets it will pour out 2 cubic metres of liquid oxygen, which is all the oxygen in this amount of air. At another outlet it will fill a gasholder with 70 cubic metres an hour of argon, from which it is taken at frequent intervals for compression into cylinders. Another outlet emits a mixture of neon and helium from which pure neon can be made if needed. A fourth outlet is used intermittently to draw off small amounts of krypton and xenon when it is necessary to separate these from the liquid oxygen where they normally exist in small quantities. A fifth outlet is opened periodically to blow down water which has had to be removed from the air before it turned to ice and damaged the plant's smooth operation. Some more water is evaporated off as steam from the alumina driers which are needed to get the air really free from water. Another nuisance material in air is carbon dioxide. This is trapped in a caustic soda scrubber in the forms of carbonate and bicarbonate of soda; it could be driven back into the atmosphere by roasting the soda carbonates to reform them into caustic soda, but normally it is run to waste. Finally, the biggest outlet of all emits 6,400 cubic metres per hour of nitrogen. There are some plants with facilities for drawing off liquid nitrogen for general use as a coolant, but the necessary modifications to the plant are barely paid for by the sales of liquid nitrogen. A better use for the waste nitrogen of an air separation plant would be to combine it chemically with hydrogen to make nitrogenous fertilizers for farming. This productive use requires a big supply of hydrogen and also of sulphur dioxide to make the fertilizer in a manageable form—powdered ammonium sulphate.

Air is such a mixture of substances that the process of separating it is very complicated. Its composition, by weight, is 75 per cent nitrogen, 23 per cent oxygen, 1·26 per cent argon, 0·7 per cent water vapour (approximately), and 0·04 per cent carbon dioxide. There are also minor constituents which cannot be neglected in view of the great quantities of air treated by a separation plant. These are 0·0012 per cent or 12 parts per million of neon, 1 p.p.m. krypton, 1·7 p.p.m. helium, 0·4 p.p.m. xenon and 0·04 p.p.m. hydrogen (p.p.m. is a common abbreviation for parts per million). Only the 0·04 p.p.m. of hydrogen is treated as negligible since hydrogen is produced very cheaply, by quite different processes, and since it is one of the few constituents which do not interfere with the operation of the plant. Even now we have not finished.

In towns, where many of the air separation plants are sited, there is atmospheric pollution. This is extremely variable, but on a hazy winter day the smoke in the air may amount to 1 p.p.m., and there will be a rather greater amount of sulphur dioxide. The smoke is taken from the air, along with any gritty particles caught up by the intake fans, in filters designed to protect the pumping machinery from abrasives. The sulphur dioxide is removed, willy nilly, in the carbon dioxide scrubber to which we shall come presently.

The flow process for the separation of air is made up of a number of subprocesses which are put together and "balanced" against each other so that the whole thing would almost go on and on for ever. We have to consider separately each of the following: air filtration, compression, scrubbing, water traps, drying, heat exchange, cooling, boilers and condensers, and rectification.

Filtration. In chemistry laboratories, filter papers are used extensively for separating solids from liquids. Another device is the sintered filter made of a small slab of a material which is really a large number of tiny glass spheres partly fused together. The holes between the spheres or between the fibres of the filter paper are of course smaller than the particles being filtered. The same sorts of material are used for filtering smoke and grit from the air, but luckily many particles are caught which are much smaller than the holes available for them to pass through. This happens because the tiny currents of air really rush quite fast through the interstices. The molecules of air travel this erratic course fairly easily; it makes little difference to them because even in static conditions they collide frequently with each other and with solid objects in their path. The particles of smoke and grit, though small, are very much bigger than molecules. At places where the general flow of air takes a sharp bend they continue straight, collide with a fibre of the filter, and perhaps stick there. Every fibre is covered with a layer one or two molecules thick of air molecules. When a relatively huge particle of dust comes along, it easily pushes these sticking air molecules aside, impinges on the solid structure of the fibre itself, and quite possibly sticks there permanently.

Industrial air filters have to be renewed frequently, because they become choked by the particles they collect until the pumps can no longer draw air through them. They are made of cheap expendable materials like wood and vegetable fibres.

Compressors are machines which take gas into a cylinder, squeeze it into a small space with a piston, and expel it into a pipe system where it travels along in its compressed state to somewhere where it is needed. A bicycle pump compresses the air in its barrel to about a quarter before pushing it through the rubber valve into the inner tube where it expands to about half its original volume. The pressure in the tyre reaches about 2 atmospheres before it is ready to roll.

In air separation plants, as soon as the air has been filtered it is compressed to about 10 atmospheres, chiefly because from now on it will need only one-tenth the space of uncompressed air. As we have seen in earlier chapters, compression heats up the air, and so it is cooled by passing it through coils round which cold water circulates. Because this water inevitably warms up it is re-cooled by outdoor air in cooling towers, so that it can be used again and not run to waste.

Scrubbing of a gas by a liquid is a common process in industry, because it has the advantages of continuity and speed. The liquid is sprayed into the top of a tower filled with open packing—glass marbles may be thought of as constituting the packing, but there are better shapes than spheres and better materials than glass. The liquid therefore trickles down the open interstices of the packing, collects at the bottom, from where it is drawn off, prepared for recirculation and used again. The process we have in mind, scrubbing the carbon dioxide out of the air, is only one of many for which the technique is employed. The scrubbing liquid in our case is dilute caustic soda and it has no commercial value when "spent". It has to be run to waste, but it is too alkaline to be run into a drain or river. The air separation company has either to buy hydrochloric acid to neutralize it, or make a deal with some neighbouring company that produces acid waste!

Water Traps. The air has already been compressed to 10 atmospheres pressure before it is scrubbed free from carbon dioxide. Next it is compressed in three stages to 160 atmospheres, and after each stage it has to be cooled by water coolers. One interesting effect of compression is that it causes quite a lot of the water originally in the air in the form of vapour to condense. Any given volume can hold only a certain amount of water vapour, depending on the temperature; this amount is not affected by the other gases present or by their pressure. Thus when air containing water vapour is squeezed into one-sixteenth its volume most of the water vapour has no alternative but to condense into liquid, up to fifteen-sixteenths of it in fact. A suitably placed catchpot will collect this condensed water. When it is nearly full a valve at the bottom is opened, and the 160 atmospheres pressure above blows down a powerful jet of water until the catchpot is empty again. There is a catchpot after each stage of the compression, to prevent the condensed water from entering the next compressor.

Alumina Driers. Even the small amount of water vapour remaining is a potential source of trouble, but fortunately there are several chemicals which have a strong affinity for water, such as quicklime and silica gel. The best of these and easiest to use is alumina, powdered aluminium oxide. The nearly dry air is passed up a tower packed with alumina, and it comes out absolutely dry. After a time the alumina becomes too damp to absorb water at the speed required. Two valves are turned, and the air is routed through a second tower. The first tower is "regenerated" by blowing hot waste nitrogen through it until the alumina returns to its original dry state.

Heat exchangers are essential to the economy of many manufacturing processes, whenever temperatures are required which are a long way either above or below normal factory temperature. Great care has been lavished on their design, because they are expensive to make, and a slight miscalculation may land the manufacturer with one which is inefficient or, on the other hand, unnecessarily big.

For amusement only, you may consider making one for your hot and cold water taps in the kitchen (Fig. 10.1). When it is fitted to the taps, and both are turned on full, the idea is that water from the hot tap shall run out cold, and water from the cold tap shall run out hot. As a first trial you might assemble two 6 ft metal pipes one inside the other; the inner one, say, being of copper and having an inside diameter of $\frac{1}{4}$ in. and the outer one being of a soft metal composition ("compo") and having an inside diameter of $\frac{3}{8}$ to $\frac{1}{2}$ in. Find some way of joining the top end of the copper pipe to the cold tap and the *bottom* end of the compo pipe to the hot tap. (This is not at all easy: you will have to make either one or two brass pieces with side arms and solder them to the pipes.) The outer pipe ought now to be wrapped with cloth heat insulation and, for compactness, the whole double

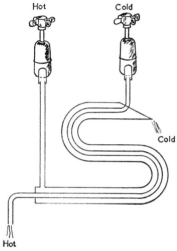

Fig. 10.1. Magic in the kitchen.

pipe should be wound into a spiral. What you hope to achieve is the following: when the cold tap is turned full on, water will try to rush down the copper pipe, but will find it rather too narrow for streamline flow, so it will run down in a turbulent fashion, eddying as it goes. The turbulence must inevitably slow down the rate of emergence of water from the outlet, but if the dimensions are correct it will not be *too* slow. The turbulence is necessary, however, to make sure that each molecule of water makes many collisions with the copper wall of the tube on its way down, so that it can achieve the temperature of the tube, whatever this may be. Similarly when the hot tap is turned full on, the hot water must flow turbulently up the space between the compo wall and the copper wall. If all is well, the copper wall will quickly develop a temperature gradient along its length, cold at the top and hot at the bottom. Both the liquid streams should be so turbulent that their temperatures are everywhere the same as that of the copper wall. Result: the stream from the cold tap will come out hot, and from the hot tap it will come out cold.

The same result can be achieved with a hot and a cold gas, or with a gas and a liquid at different temperatures, but of course the dimensions of the pipes are different for each material. Industrial heat exchangers are similar in principle, but they are not always made of pipes within pipes. It is largely due to the heat exchangers that the waste nitrogen emerging from a first class air separation plant is not cold, although it has only recently evaporated from the liquid, but within a degree or two of the temperature of the ingoing air.

Cooling in an air separation plant is carried out by two of the methods in Chapter Six: external work by a gas, and internal work producing Joule-Thomson cooling. The plant requires a mixture of liquid and gaseous air to flow continuously into a *boiler* where its temperature must be $-172°C$ and its pressure $5·5$ atmospheres. To achieve this, a stream of air at 160 atm. is first cooled in a heat exchanger to $-16°C$. The stream is divided into two, 60 per cent of it going into an expansion engine where its great pressure drives pistons which are themselves driving a dynamo. The air emerges from the expansion engine at $-150°C$ and $5·5$ atm., ready to join the other part of the stream. Note that $-150°C$ is not cold enough for liquid to be formed anywhere in the expansion engine—a piston sliding into a cylinder, for example, would be terribly jarred (and something would break) if it suddenly came up against a body of liquid in the head of the cylinder. The 40 per cent fraction of the air stream is cooled in another heat exchanger from $-16°C$ to $-170°C$, and then allowed to expand through a throttling valve, doing internal work. As a result it cools to $-172°C$ and part of it liquefies. Its pressure is now $5·5$ atm., and it is rejoined by the 60 per cent stream. The united stream of gas with some liquid passes into the boiler.

Boilers in an air separation plant are all extremely cold, and it would be wasteful to supply them with any kind of external heat such as an electric immersion heater. Of the three different boilers in a typical plant, one (the one mentioned just above) is a mere reservoir of boiling liquid with no heater at all, and it is kept boiling by the continuous stream of gaseous and liquid air passing into it. The second contains nearly pure liquid oxygen boiling at −180°C and 1·3 atm. It is heated by the condensation outside it of a gas which is rich in nitrogen, at 5·5 atm. (If a flask of cold water is held in the steam from a boiling kettle, the steam condenses on the outside of the flask and the cold water warms up; the principle is the same.) The third boiler in the plant is for boiling a mixture of oxygen, krypton and xenon at such a temperature that the oxygen boils but the other two, which are much less volatile, remain liquid. It is heated by an immersed coil through which passes air at −172°C and 5·5 atm.

Rectifying columns are used in all sorts of industries—oil refineries, distilleries, and gas separation plants. Before you can own one, you need a licence from the Board of Customs and Excise, because they could be used for the production of illicit alcohol. They are by far the best equipment for separating mixtures of two (or more) substances when they have nearly equal boiling points. Water–alcohol, butane–higher-hydrocarbons, and oxygen–nitrogen are three such mixtures, but there are many more.

In the heat exchanger, it will be remembered, there is a turbulent stream of fluid going up, and another coming down. The two streams are separated by a copper wall, and this has a steady temperature gradient from top to bottom. So have the two streams, and the down-coming fluid warms up while the up-going fluid cools down. (In the kitchen tap example, this was the way the taps were connected to the pipes, but the connections could have been reversed with the same result.)

In a rectifying column there is a continuous downward flow of a liquid and an upward flow of a gas, but there is no copper wall between them. The gas flow is made turbulent by the liquid droplets falling through it and by other obstructions. The liquid flows or trickles under its own weight among glass marbles or some other packing similar to that used in scrubbers. Because both the up and the down flow are turbulent, there is temperature equilibrium at all levels, and there is a steady temperature gradient all the way down the column. At the bottom the trickling liquid drips into a reservoir of boiling liquid and, as it boils, keeps up the supply of vapour to flow upwards against the stream of liquid. The temperature is highest at the bottom, and lowest at the top of the column, where there is a condenser—a cold surface on which the stream of vapour condenses.

Are the gas and liquid the same in constitution then ? Not at all. They contain the same two (or more) constituents, but in different proportions. Moreover, the gas is changing in constitution as it goes up, and the liquid as it comes down. Remember that the liquid and gas have every opportunity to impinge on each other everywhere in the column. They not only exchange heat if their temperatures are the least bit different, they exchange molecules too. If a drop of liquid, a mixture of two substances of different boiling points, has to give up a molecule to the gas around it, the molecule will most likely be from the more volatile component. Likewise if the gas, a mixture of two components, has to allow a molecule to condense on to a nearby drop, the molecule will most likely be of the substance with lower boiling point. In consequence of all this, the liquid in the boiler changes to the high boiling point constituent, and the vapour at the top of the column to the low boiling point constituent. Between the top and bottom there is a "composition gradient" in the liquid and another in the vapour.

A little thought will show that some way up the column there must be a point where the liquid has the same composition as the raw material, whatever it is, which must be "rectified". Now imagine that at this level the raw material is fed in continuously as a liquid, through sprays so that its droplets join those coming down the column. Imagine also that vapour is continuously drawn off from the top of the column (so that only some of it is allowed to re-condense) and liquid is continuously drawn off from the boiler (so that only some of it is allowed to reboil). The combined mass of the liquid and vapour drawn off must be kept equal to the mass of raw material fed in. Many other working conditions must be satisfied, depending on the particular rectification being done, but you now have a continuous working rectifying column.

So long as his column pours out the products he requires, the manufacturer does not bother too much what are its details of operation. He knows if he has to change the feed rate, for instance, that he must also meddle with the heat input to the boiler, the cooling circulation through the condenser, and the withdrawal rates at the top and bottom of the column; and that the system will take hours, and possibly days, to settle down to its new steady state. The academic design engineers, on the other hand, would like to know *all* about rectifying columns, or even all about one large rectifying column. They cannot experiment with that of the manufacturer, for they would very seriously upset his productivity. They cannot build and use their own, for if they did they would produce so much valuable rectified material that they would have to go into business. It is not surprising, therefore, that many of the important "theoretical" properties of rectifying columns are still not understood (although of course many others have already been thoroughly studied). The fact is that a big rectifying column is a sort of Leviathan, an animal whose limbs move slowly but irresistibly in response to any stimulus from the world outside it; the stimuli from within, any hunger or pain that it feels, and whatever goes on in its brain, are unfathomable, chiefly because of the very long delay between any stimulus and the corresponding response.

Air Separation

The main part of an air-separation plant is illustrated in Fig. 10.2. After our somewhat lengthy examination of the various

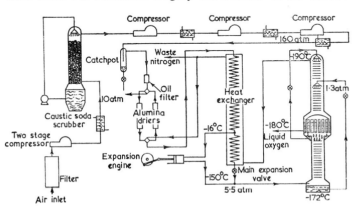

Fig. 10.2. Air separation plant.

components of this plant, the figure nearly explains itself. Everything in it has already been described, except the arrangement of the double rectifying column on the right.

The lower part of this column receives at the bottom its feed supply of a mixture of oxygen and nitrogen liquid and oxygen and nitrogen gas, all at 5·5 atm. pressure. It partly separates them into an oxygen-rich liquid at the bottom and a nitrogen-rich liquid at the top. Both these liquids are fed into the upper part of the column. Notice which liquid is fed into the top and which about half way down (the droplets coming down the upper column have to be nearly pure nitrogen at the top, changing gradually as they fall into nearly pure oxygen at the bottom).

Notice also that the boiling reservoir of liquid oxygen at the bottom of the upper column provides underneath itself a surface on which the nitrogen-rich mixture in the lower column can condense. Conversely, the condensation of this nitrogen-rich mixture keeps the liquid oxygen on the boil. At first sight this might seem to be impossible: how can boiling liquid oxygen be at the same temperature as condensing nitrogen, when their normal boiling points differ by 13°C? The answer is of course that we are not concerned with normal boiling points at atmospheric pressure; −180°C is the boiling point of oxygen at 1·3 atm. pressure, and also the boiling point of nitrogen, at 5·5 atm. pressure.

The figure naturally omits a lot of important detail. It shows the three most important valves where there is a big reduction in pressure, but at either side of each valve there should be a pressure gauge. In addition, the plant has many other control valves, pressure gauges, thermometers, and safety devices for the use and protection of the engineers and other staff working the plant.

Furthermore, the figure gives no information about the separation of the rare gases from air, although this is done right inside the main plant. The necessary attachments are shown separately in Fig. 10.3. The rare gases accumulate at three different places according to their boiling points. Helium and neon, which boil at much lower temperatures than any reached in the plant, collect where the nitrogen-rich gas is condensing at the top of the lower column. They must be drawn off to allow up-coming gases to reach the condensing surface, and they are freed from residual nitrogen gas in a cooling tower through whose cooling coil passes nitrogen at the lower pressure.

Argon has a normal boiling point only 3°C below that of oxygen. It accumulates as gas mixed with oxygen-rich gas, towards the bottom of the upper column. It has to be separated in a highly efficient column of its own, where the oxygen mixed with it is made to condense. Krypton and xenon accumulate in the liquid oxygen at the bottom of the upper column. They are separated in a column of their own. The heater for this column, and

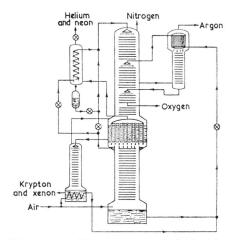

Fig. 10.3. Auxiliary separators attached to the double rectifying column.

the condenser for the argon column, are kept at the right temperatures by a gas and a liquid respectively, circulated from convenient points in the plant system. To separate krypton from xenon, and neon from helium, methods of selective adsorption are used.

The value to industry of the separated constituents of air is enormous. Steelworks and certain chemical plants use oxygen in large quantities, but they use it as gas, for welding and cutting apparatus and for chemical oxidation. Some firms have their oxygen delivered as liquid, and store it in tanks having built-in evaporating coils of tube, through which it can be driven out as gas when needed. Other firms make their own nearly pure oxygen, with a much simplified form of the plant depicted in Fig. 10·2, which economizes energy by delivering the oxygen as gas nearly at room temperature. Some of these "tonnage" oxygen machines produce 250 tons of oxygen per day.

Whereas oxygen is used to burn acetylene in extremely hot blowlamp flames, for welding and cutting, argon is used at the same time to prevent burning. The welding or cutting flame is intended to heat a small part of a steel assembly very quickly to its melting point, but it is not quick enough to prevent neighbouring metal from getting hot by conduction. If this metal is in contact with air it will oxidize or even ignite, and to prevent spoilage of this kind a jet of argon is directed around the flame. Krypton is used in great quantities for filling electric lamp bulbs. It is inert, and does not react with the white hot tungsten filaments or their coating of rare-earth oxides; but above all, it is a bad conductor of heat, and the filament can maintain its temperature without too large an electric current, and without making the glass bulb unbearably hot. The other rare gases are used in small quantities, because their pressure is only a few thousandths of an atmosphere, in discharge lamps for neon signs, street lighting and other special applications.

In this chapter, only a single example has been given of gas separation by cooling. Other examples would be tedious to treat in detail, but their main purposes are worth knowing. Ammonia synthesis gas has to be a mixture of three volumes of hydrogen with one volume of nitrogen, and very little else; in particular there must be no carbon monoxide since this "poisons" the catalyst which speeds up the combination of hydrogen and nitrogen to form ammonia. The correct mixture can be made, starting with coke-oven gas and compressed nitrogen, or starting with methane, oxygen and nitrogen; in either case cooling to liquid air temperatures is necessary. Another chemical important as a raw material is ethylene, which can be made by heating petroleum liquids in an oil refinery. It has to be freed from a long list of other gases unfortunately produced at the same time, and this is achieved in a lengthy process in which all the gases except hydrogen are liquefied.

The use of cold for purifying gas mixtures has increased recently, and will probably increase much further. As we have seen, it can be applied in all sorts of flow procesess, where the raw materials pour steadily in at one end, and the products pour steadily out. These flow processes are ideal for making materials in the large quantities required by both the modern householder and the modern industrialist.

Chapter Eleven

COLD FUELS

A LIQUEFIED GAS can be transported anywhere, nowadays, much
more easily than the same amount of gas compressed in cylinders.
The reason is simple. A cylinder to hold 5,000 litres of gas,
suitably compressed, weighs 100 kilos, 220 lb. The same amount
of gas, liquefied, occupies 6 or 7 litres, and can be carried in two
large glass vacuum flasks of total weight less than 5 kg, or 11 lb.
These are fairly small quantities, but on a much larger scale the
comparison is much the same. Huge cylinders for holding gases
at the highest safe pressure cannot compete with large well
insulated metal vessels for storing the liquefied gas.

We have seen how liquid oxygen is now carried by road, even
when it has to be converted to gas at its destination before it can
be used. More often than not, it is then used to burn things, as a
supporter of combustion. The same idea is coming into use for
carrying gaseous fuels, and it is enabling gases to be used as fuels
in situations where they were most unsuitable before modern
liquefaction techniques became practicable. One such use is as
rocket propellants.

Toy rockets use for propellant a form of gunpowder, which is a
mixture of fuel (charcoal dust and sulphur) and oxidizer (saltpetre). When the propellant is ignited, the mixture burns without
using oxygen from the air: the fuel combines violently with
oxygen from the saltpetre, and products are shot downwards, and
the rest of the rocket shoots upwards. In a sense it is wrong to
speak of fuel in this context. Any reagents would do, provided
they react violently enough and generate gaseous products.
Hydrogen and fluorine are a pair of reagents which fulfil these
requirements, and it is only by convention that hydrogen is
termed the "fuel" and fluorine the "oxidant".

Many considerations combine to determine which is the best
pair of reagents for use in a rocket, but first one needs to know their
specific impulse. For every gram of combustion products shot out
of the tail of the rocket, how much push is given to the rocket?

The specific impulse of nitric acid, with ammonia or an organic fuel, is round about 240 seconds (the second is the unit of specific impulse, and it results from dividing the unit of impulse by the unit of mass). If nitric acid as oxidant is replaced by hydrogen peroxide the specific impulse is about 5 per cent higher, and another 7 per cent is gained by using liquid oxygen. The really big gain comes from using liquid hydrogen as the fuel, for which there is no extra technical difficulty in using liquid oxygen as the oxidant; the specific impulse is then 364 seconds. Even this is not quite the most powerful combination available; liquid hydrogen and liquid fluorine together give a specific impulse of 373 seconds. However, fluorine is very difficult to handle, and the product of the reaction is hydrogen fluoride, the most corrosive acid for concrete, glass and many other materials, so a very special rocket launching site would be needed.

The satellites now orbiting the earth have been launched with liquid oxygen and a hydrocarbon fuel, similar to paraffin or kerosene. Much experimental work has been done, and is continuing, to permit liquid hydrogen to be used as fuel. At a large test site in Nevada there are two liquid hydrogen vessels, each holding 50,000 gallons, inside a three foot thickness of perlite insulation (perlite is a granulated form of expanded mica). The loss by evaporation is only 0·3 per cent per day, but every time the liquid is pumped along the 8 in. diameter pipelines to an experimental rig 50 yards away, 10,000 gallons of liquid hydrogen are evaporated simply in cooling down the pipeline.

The technology of rocketry has advanced a long way since an American first used liquid oxygen in a rocket in 1926. With the coming of nuclear reactors, there is the possibility of using liquid hydrogen alone as the propellant, without bothering to burn it. Fig. 11.1 shows a simplified design of an oxygen-hydrogen combustion rocket, with liquid oxygen in the upper chamber.

In a typical design for a reactor rocket, liquid hydrogen is vapourized and heated in a reactor chamber, where its pressure builds up to about double that of the gases in a combustion chamber. When it rushes out of the expansion nozzle, its specific impulse could be three or four times the 364 seconds previously mentioned.

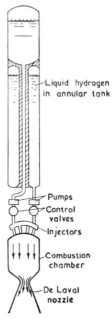

Fig. 11.1. An oxygen-hydrogen rocket.

Liquid Methane

So much can be said for the possibilities of very cold liquid
fuels for interplanetary travel, where overall costs are so high
that the difficulty of handling these awkward fuels is not pro-
hibitive. But in the more mundane application of gas to domestic
uses, a very cold liquid is already playing an important part. The
task of supplying Britain with domestic and industrial fuel gas
has for many years been a big industry. Since the late 1800s this
gas has been made from coal and coke by processes which are
clumsy, dirty and smelly. In countries with underground sources
of petroleum and methane, these gas works have been largely
supplemented and even superseded by supplies of natural gas,
which often contains a high proportion of the powerful fuel,
methane (CH_4). Britain is just beginning to obtain gas from under
the North Sea, but it is already importing quite a lot of methane
from North Africa. During trials of the first tanker to be specially

designed for this purpose, liquefied methane was brought from even farther away, from Venezuela. What, then, are the problems of bringing such a difficult fuel so far, how are they being solved, and how much does it cost?

Natural gas is used all over the United States and Canada, and there are gas wells in operation in seven out of the eleven Canadian provinces. It is being exploited in at least 18 other countries, distributed all over the world. Besides methane, it usually contains some hydrogen sulphide, petroleum hydrocarbons, carbon dioxide, nitrogen and other materials. The hydrogen sulphide must be removed before the gas comes into contact with steel, because it is highly active, rendering most steels as brittle as glass; in any case hydrogen sulphide is a valuable chemical since sulphur in its many compounds is in great demand.

After any purification that may be necessary, the residue is chiefly methane, which boils at $-160°C$ or $113°K$. It solidifies at $89°K$. Its critical temperature is $-82°C$, so it cannot be liquefied by direct compression unless it is cooled below room temperatures. At $0°C$ it needs a pressure of 140 atmospheres, which is inconveniently large. When the method of compression and boiling is used for methane it is done by a "cascade" system in three stages:

(1) Ammonia is compressed, cooled with water until it liquefies, and circulated through the heat exchanger of stage (2).

(2) Ethylene is compressed, cooled with liquid ammonia until it liquefies, and circulated through the heat exchanger of stage (3).

(3) Methane is compressed, cooled with liquid ethylene until it liquefies; and its pressure is reduced to atmospheric whereupon part of the liquid boils but in doing so cools the remainder to its normal boiling point of $113°K$.

A cascade system is used in Russia for liquefying up to 70 tons per day, and the liquid methane is transported by lorries to a chemical plant 50 km away, each lorry load being 1 ton of the liquid. (It is a rather bulky liquid, having a density only 0·72 times that of water.)

The Joule-Thomson expansion method is also used for liquefying methane. It consumes more power than the cascade system, but the plant is smaller and cheaper, and water is the only coolant needed.

Evidently the producer of natural gas has one set of problems, the distributor of fuel gas a second set, and the transporter of liquid methane a third set. Only when all three sets of problems have been solved can natural gas from the Sahara or Venezuela be delivered to the householder or industrial user in England. The producer has to draw the crude gas from underground, dispatch it (by pipeline) to the refinery which will be near the wharf at which tankers are loaded. Here, at a convenient rate, commercial methane of an agreed standard of purity is made, along with other products such as sulphur. The methane is piped to the liquefying plant, which has the task of filling the storage tanks with liquid methane and refilling them whenever a tanker has taken its cargo. The storage tanks are at the loading wharf, specially constructed with wide, heavily insulated pipelines for conveying the liquid methane to the tanker moored alongside. Whenever a transfer is made, it begins with parts of the equipment at a much higher temperature than the liquid methane, and the only way for this to be cooled is by the boiling of the methane itself. As much "cold" as possible has to be extracted from the boiling liquid and from the cold vapour it produces, and the warm gas is returned along a separate gas pipeline to the gasholders from which it can be taken and reliquefied. For the first experimental shipment of 2,000 tons of liquid methane a converted oil tanker was used, and it took about 10 days to cool the tanks sufficiently to receive the liquid methane. There was also the liquid pipeline to be cooled. However, when the ship returned for its second filling, no cooling was necessary, because 5 per cent of the original liquid methane had been left in the tanks to keep them cold.

The purchaser and distributor of the methane thus transported was, and is, the North Thames Gas Board. The installation for receiving the fuel is at Canvey Island in the Thames estuary. There is no question of boiling the methane as it leaves the ship and piping it away as gas or storing it in gasholders: the ship would have to wait for weeks while this was done, and hundreds of gasholders would be needed. Instead, the methane is pumped as liquid into storage tanks each of which holds 1,000 tons. They are made of welded aluminium alloy, fifty feet in diameter and fifty feet high, and they cost about £500,000 each. Round each inner tank is a steel shell, with a 2 ft gap between, and the gap is filled with a granular insulating material. The installation at

Canvey Island also includes a 2,000 ft long aluminium pipeline, with six inches of insulation, and a big (100,000 cu ft) gasholder to receive the methane which boils off during transfer.

Thirdly, there are the ships for carrying the liquid methane. These are specially built vessels whose sole occupation is to fetch the valuable cargo and return in ballast. Their most economical size is such that they carry 20,000 tons of methane, and their tanks of welded aluminium have to be strengthened to withstand the most violent motion they are likely to encounter at sea. Even the insulation needs to be stronger than normal, and in the first experimental ship balsa-wood was used. The methane tankers carry their own pumps for charging and discharging their cargo, and largely as a safety measure they are able to reliquefy the 0·5 per cent of methane which boils off during a journey.

The economics of importing methane, as far as Britain is concerned, is dependent on the cost of making gas by traditional methods, compared with the cost of buying liquid methane, of transporting it, and of storing and processing it (including evaporating it and mixing it with inert gases to reduce its calorific value to the statutory 500 Btu per cubic foot). Although the total capital requirement is £50m for a reasonable sized system, importing 1·5 million tons per year, the cost is only about two-thirds of home made gas. As a result the British gas industry hopes to keep prices steady or reduce them for some years to come, instead of increasing them in step with wages, salaries and the price of other commodities.

Hazards of Cold Fuels

Precautions, instruments and warning devices are the lifeline of the worker with liquefied fuels. The main danger is that the liquid will somehow burst out of its container, evaporate, and explode or burn. There was a terrible accident in Cleveland, U.S.A. in 1944 when a tank of liquid natural gas fractured. Possibly the failure was because hydrogen sulphide in the liquid had reacted with the steel of the tank and made it brittle; the steel may then have fractured in the vibration of a slight earthquake shock. Nearly a million gallons of evaporating liquid ran out over the site and neighbouring land inevitably catching fire. In the heat a second storage tank collapsed and another 300,000 gallons of fuel were added to the conflagration. The death roll was 128, and a further 400 people were injured. About £2·5m worth of property was destroyed. There have been many fires, before and since, in which fuel stores have gone up, but this is the only major case in which the prime cause was the liquid nature of a liquefied fuel gas.

Chapter Twelve

COLD IN BIOLOGY AND MEDICINE

LIVING THINGS ARE all more or less sensitive to cold, though many are much more adaptable than man. Not long after freezing mixtures were invented, scientists were experimenting with the effect of very severe cold on animals, and they at once discovered some surprising results. Just over 300 years ago Henry Power took a jar of vinegar which was infested with minute eels and froze it solid. On remelting nearly three hours later the eels which had been "incrystalled, danced and frisked about as lively as ever". Frogs, small fish and caterpillars were found to survive moderately long freezing in ice, but careful observers proved that they all retained some liquid at least inside their bodies.

Travellers from the Arctic brought dramatic tales of insects, molluscs, reptiles and fish, frozen for long periods, which revived completely after being thawed. A certain variety of caterpillar survived four successive exposures to temperatures between $-11°C$ and $-47°C$. Alaskan blackfish, which had been stored in blocks of ice, were chopped out and fed to the sledge dogs. Shortly after some of the dogs vomited up the fish which had been thawed and had come back to life in the warmth of the stomach. People began to hope that a way would be found of storing animals of any kind in the frozen state, and of resuscitating them at some future date. This would have been cheating Father Time indeed.

A French professor in the 1930s showed that goldfish could be immersed in liquid air at about $-190°C$ for up to 15 seconds without fatal results. He also showed how a skilful conjurer could deceive an audience into believing that these goldfish had been immersed much longer, like other specimens which had become brittle right through, and which the professor had snapped in half. However, some people in the audience went away believing the whole experiment to be genuine, and the consequence was that for many years the professor's goldfish remained an unsolved scientific mystery. Many fish were tested and found to survive formation of sufficient ice in the skin and superficial tissues to make the body stiff and hard, so long as their deep body temperature did not fall too low. If their internal organs became frozen, the fish always died. One variety of fish, the small vinegar eel, could be cooled right through to $-190°C$ and survived if it was warmed up very quickly. For some reason the body water did not turn to ice but became vitrified, but if the warming up occurred slowly, crystals of ice formed at about $-40°C$ and the fish was killed.

There are some minute animals which can lose all their body water, and survive. If these animals, after being completely desiccated, are cooled even to liquid helium temperatures and kept there indefinitely, they revive fully after rewarming and moistening. Unfortunately, most other animals cannot tolerate the loss of even a proportion of their body water, so experiments of this kind have limited use.

Recent experiments have revealed how widely differing animals manage to avoid freezing all through. Some do so by keeping their body liquids supercooled, i.e. liquid although cooler than their true freezing point. These include frogs, toads, lizards, tortoises and snakes, and they can survive supercooling to between $-5°C$ and $-10°C$. People are now wondering whether they ever become supercooled during their natural hibernation, but there is a lot of evidence that frogs, for example, ultimately succumb in a long spell of low temperature. Probably those which survive the bitter north Canadian winter do so by burying themselves in mud which, though it freezes, retains a temperature above $-1°C$.

Glycerol

Some insects have a much more powerful method of resisting cold. Their larvae and prepupae have to hibernate at much lower temperatures, and Japanese investigators found that about one third of a certain variety survived immersion in liquid oxygen at $-180°C$. They were able to isolate the hearts of some of these insects and study with a microscope the effect of cooling the hearts, immersed in blood, to $-20°C$. Ice crystals formed outside the hearts, which lost water and shrank, but did not freeze. The fundamental trick which these insects use, to prevent freezing of vital organs, was discovered in 1957. Physiologists found their bodies to contain large quantities of glycerol, up to 25 per cent.

Glycerol is an alcohol which has a tremendous affinity for water, and is usually obtained as a viscous liquid though its freezing point is $+18°C$. It is used in a great number of medical preparations. When a solution of glycerol in water freezes, the ice appears in a shape resembling quill feathers, and unfrozen liquid remains in the spaces. The concentration of glycerol increases in the liquid until it is two-thirds glycerol, and then its freezing point should be $-47°C$. However, even below this temerpature, in the presence of ice crystals, the liquid will remain supercooled and not freeze.

Nearly ten years before glycerol was discovered to be a natural protection against cold, it had been found to have similar applications in the laboratory, by a lucky accident. A group of biologists at Mill Hill, London, were trying to preserve semen for breeding purposes. Dr Audrey Smith, in her book *Biological effects of freezing and supercooling*, writes: "After several months of intensive work we were still unable to preserve the fertilizing capacity of the cock semen for more than 8–12 hr *in vitro* at any temperature above zero and we therefore returned to the problem of storing the spermatozoa at low temperatures. A bottle labelled laevulose was taken out of the cold store and was again used as a semen diluent. Contrary to expectation, the spermatozoa survived cooling to and rewarming from $-79°C$. Freshly prepared solutions of laevulose were, as before, completely ineffective in protecting against damage during freezing and thawing. At first we suspected that a mould, which had grown in the solution during storage, must have been responsible for the change in its biological properties and for the absence of reducing sugars. The solution was then analysed by Dr D. Elliott who found that it contained approximately 10 per cent glycerol and 1 per cent albumen. We were puzzled by this result until we realized that we had been freezing the spermatozoa in the solution of Meyer's histological albumen originally used in preparing smears of spermatozoa for staining and microscopy. The crystal of thymol, normally added to inhibit growth of bacteria and moulds, had been omitted from the solution and it had therefore been stored in the cold together with the original laevulose solution. It had then been forgotten, and during storage the labels from th bottles must have dropped off and been exchanged." A careful systematic investigation was now made, which showed that glycerol, and not albumen, was the protective constituent. The glycerol was effective not only against cold, but against the removal of 80 to 90 per cent of the water at low temperatures.

The events which have just been described marked the beginning of an important advance in animal husbandry. By 1951 chicks had been reared from eggs laid by pullets which had been inseminated with semen frozen to, kept at, and thawed from $-190°C$ in a solution containing 15 per cent glycerol. The glycerol had been removed by dialysis before insemination. Intensive tests were already being made on the use of glycerol to store the semen from mice, rats, rabbits, guinea pigs, rams and bulls. By 1953 the way was opened for application to the cattle breeding industry of a method of long term storage of bull semen at very low temperatures. Although much remained to be investigated, and although the method then used was not necessarily the only or the best system, "banks" or stores of frozen semen had already been established at centres in different parts of Britain. Farmers could select semen from bulls which might not have been available when required. Valuable semen was no longer wasted, and semen from bulls of uncertain value could be stored for several years until their progeny had matured and been tested for milk yield and other qualities. Another potential advantage of the method was that, during epidemics of infections such as foot and mouth disease, there would be a reserve of semen previously collected which could be used until all danger of further contagion had passed. The banks of semen at low temperatures would permit economy in the number of bulls used for breeding within one country and, internationally, the possibility was opened up of vigorous trade in semen to improve stock throughout the world.

By 1960 the glycerol method of low temperature storage had been perfected, and even controlled in such a way as to destroy at the same time certain pathogenic organisms liable to infect the inseminated cow. Similar techniques are being evolved more slowly for the semen of other large, slow breeding animals, including man. Early results with sheep, horses and pigs were disappointing, showing that much more systematic investigation was needed. The spermatozoa of man seem to be more resistant to freezing than those of any other mammal. Only a very few cases of actual use of the method have been reported, all offspring being normal, but methods have been proposed which would increase the chances of children being born to the wife of a sub-fertile husband.

It has been said that artificial insemination has abolished time and space in cattle breeding—calves may be born from bulls long dead or at the other side of the world—and traditional methods have already diminished in importance. Scientifically, however, the bull semen work is only a small and comparatively minor part of the researches which have arisen out of the discovery of the protective properties of glycerol, and the abolition of time and space by low temperatures.

One form of life has so far been left unmentioned, the micro-organisms which we often ignore, but which account for much more than half the weight of living material on earth. Some of them play a key part in our lives and are almost as essential as food and sunlight. Without them, living inside us, we die. Others are highly dangerous and must at all costs be kept away from the human system, or at least from that part of the body where they would multiply until they destroyed it all. It is important to have stocks of all micro-organisms, each uncontaminated by any of the others. They are normally kept in cultures, growing and multiplying, under laboratory control. In general, it would be much simpler to keep them in a state of suspended animation, or anabiosis, like the spermatozoa discussed earlier. Undoubtedly low temperature is the most obvious way of slowing down the ageing and degeneration of living cells, because the chemical reactions, respiration and metabolism, are very much retarded. Many efforts have been made, and are continuing, to employ low temperatures in this way, using glycerol and other aids if needed. In the case of yeasts, which are important in industries such as brewing, in causing and in treating diseases (penicillin being the best known therapeutic example), a different way of storing has been found. The yeast culture is covered in mineral oil and kept at room temperature, and it survives without growing for 1–3 years. This has made research on low temperature storage less urgent, but it will still be needed for elucidating the way of life of the organisms.

Hospitals

When we look for the most tangible and direct influence of low temperature biology on human life, we come without any hesitation to surgery. The first great step in surgery was the exclusion from wounds of all unwanted micro-organisms, by cleanliness and antiseptics. Another was the use of anaesthetics. The two most recent advances, comparable in importance, are blood transfusion and hypothermia. Both allow long, complicated operations to be performed in comparative safety, and both give the patient's own vital system a better chance to restore itself to normal working; and both are dependent on low temperatures for retarding metabolism and biochemical change.

Hypothermia is the more recent, but the more obvious of the two. It is medical Greek for "low body temperature", and its techniques have evolved from studies of the physiological effects of low body temperatures. The normal body temperature is 37°C, but it can be reduced to 29°C without damaging the brain and other vital organs although it reduces their supply of oxygenated blood. At this temperature the heart can be stopped for 8 minutes, and surgical operations can be performed on it in a comparatively bloodless field. The operation would be useless, however, if blood with its oxygen were to be cut off from other organs, particularly the brain, for even a fraction of a minute. This is where the heart-lung machine takes over. It has been developed in the last few years to do for short periods the work of the heart and lungs together: that is it draws carbonated blood from the arteries, drives off the carbon dioxide replacing it by oxygen, and pumps the oxygenated blood into the veins. It may be regarded as a very advanced form of blood transfusion.

Cold is coming into use in a brain operation, where it first numbs a small region of brain cells and then, if the desired response follows, it destroys the unwanted cells permanently. There is no loss of blood, and throughout the main part of the operation the patient is awake, demonstrating to the surgeon how well he can control his limbs. The illness is Parkinson's disease, which is due to a small number of disorderly cells in the brain. These prevent the sufferer from controlling properly the movement of his arms and legs. His hands have violent tremors, he has difficulty in walking, and sometimes his limbs go intolerably rigid leaving him virtually helpless.

The human body has remarkable built-in-mechanisms for putting right its performance when some part of itself is unable to function properly—for example, with parts of the knee removed people soon learn to walk and run normally. The same seems to be true for Parkinson's disease, and when the offending cells are put out of action the patient recovers fully.

There are a hundred thousand million (10^{11}) cells in the brain, but the surgeon knows approximately where the disordered cells are. They are near the middle of the thalamus, a distinct part of the brain about the size of an egg right down near the centre of the skull. The surgeon operates through a half-inch hole in the

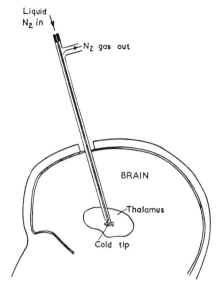

Fig. 12.1. A brain operation.

skull which he has previously made using a local anaesthetic. He locates the thalamic nucleus as closely as possible by X-ray photography, and then inserts the instrument shown in Fig. 12.1. This is really a long thin Dewar vessel of German silver, whose extreme tip is not shielded by the vacuum space. The cannula, as the instrument is called, passes between the convolutions of the brain, pushing them harmlessly aside.

A little cold is applied, by passing liquid nitrogen down the central tube to the tip, where it evaporates and escapes via the annular space between the central tube and the inner wall of the

Dewar. If the right cells have been temporarily numbed by this cooling, the patient will have already lost his tremor, and will be able to hold his hands quite steady. If the tremor is still there, the surgeon moves the tip of the cannula around and tries again, until he finds the right cells. At this stage the operation could be abandoned, and all the brain cells would return to normal activity, but the patient would be no better. However, a faster flow of liquid nitrogen is passed through the cannula for a measured period, and the extreme cold puts the disordered cells permanently out of action. From then on, the patient has normal control of his hands and limbs—he usually asks for a cup of tea and drinks it without spilling a drop. Hypothermia is also potentially useful in operations on the brain and elsewhere.

Blood transfusion began to be used successfully after the blood groups O, A, B and AB had been discovered in 1901, together with the knowledge of which groups could be mixed without coagulating. In 1914–18 many lives were saved and much experience of transfusion was gained, but blood could only be stored for short periods. By 1939 several blood banks had been established, in which blood was stored at $+5°C$ for 3–7 days, and then destroyed. The increasing use of blood transfusion made it imperative to find ways of storing it for much longer times. Plasma which had been separated from the red blood cells could be kept frozen, and it could be freeze dried, that is the ice could be allowed to evaporate into a pumped vacuum. The residual solid material could be kept for many months at room temperature; when reconstituted with water it was of some use for transfusion in cases of surgical shock. The main problem remained that of storing the red corpuscles.

Again glycerol came to the rescue. Step by step the possibilities were explored, until it was found that the red cells could be kept for a year in a medium containing an appropriate concentration of glycerol, at $-45°C$. Even longer periods might be possible at still lower temperatures, but a year is already long enough. During storage, glycerol enters through the membranes into the cells, and has to be removed again before they can be used in a transfusion. Removal speedily, and without damage to the cells, is accomplished by washing with special fluids in a high "gravitational" field in a centrifuge. About 2 hours washing is needed to prepare enough cells for one litre of blood.

Besides blood banks which ensure a plentiful supply of blood during all hospital operations and most emergencies, we have a smaller number of eye banks. These supply corneal tissue, the clear front layer of the eye, for grafting in the place of damaged corneas. Naturally the cornea is the part of the eye most liable to be damaged, and corneal grafts are a great human asset. The stock of the eye bank is maintained from the dead bodies of people who have left them by Will for surgical use. The cornea may be stored for 2–3 weeks under sterile liquid paraffin at $+4°C$, or the whole eye may be impregnated with glycerol and stored for much longer at $-79°C$, in contact with solid carbon dioxide.

These are some of the practical results of wide-ranging researches which are still going on. Experiments on the storage of nerve ganglia, hearts, kidneys and other organs have all been repeated recently with techniques using glycerol. They may only yield fresh information about the structure and function of the organs concerned, or they may lead to great new developments in surgery. From the point of view of individual human sufferers, unfortunately, these improvements are never made quickly enough. There are still many types of system defect for which the only treatment utilizes those remarkable built-in mechanisms which make a human body adapt itself to the task of living with some part of itself unable to function properly.

Chapter Thirteen

SUPERCONDUCTIVITY

WHEN KAMERLINGH ONNES liquefied helium in 1908, he and his colleagues knew that there was a great deal of work for them to do. They had to measure systematically the properties of materials at very low temperatures. Radioactivity and other nuclear properties are completely independent of temperature, but nearly all the rest, electrical, magnetic, thermal and mechanical, change considerably with lowering temperature. Some of them change very strongly in the range between liquid hydrogen temperatures, around 20°K, and liquid helium temperatures, around 4°K.

One of the earliest properties investigated in the laboratories at Leiden was the resistance of metal wires. It was measured by finding the voltage or potential difference between the ends of a wire when a known current is flowing through it as in Fig. 4.2. Whenever the current measured by A is doubled, the voltage measured by V is also doubled according to Ohm's Law, and the resistance is V/A. With some metals such as copper, iron and platinum, the resistance dropped smoothly down with falling temperature until at 4°K it was only perhaps a hundredth of its value at 0°C. With others, notably lead, mercury and tin, there was a temperature, different for each one but all well below 20°K, at which the resistance dropped to nothing at all. A hundredth of a degree above this critical temperature the resistance was normal, like those of copper, iron and platinum, but a hundredth of a degree below it was zero or too small to measure. The excitement, agitation, and checking of instruments in these sober Dutch laboratories can only be imagined, but eventually everyone was satisfied and the superconductivity (of mercury) was published as an observed fact in 1912. This result was no freak. It was reproduced and checked until, by 1962, a resistance as small as 10^{-17} ohms would have been detected, but it was not there. Nor were tin, lead and mercury freak metals. Twenty-two superconducting metals are now known, as well as numerous alloys and compounds such as certain nitrides and carbides.

The completely unforeseen phenomenon of superconductivity meant that low temperature laboratories had much more to do than long series of careful measurements "for the record". They had to find the explanation of a growing series of results which not only seemed contrary to nature as men understood it, but which did not at first fit in too well with each other. By now most of the inconsistencies have been tidied up, but a full explanation has not been found. Theoretical physicists have recently produced a promising model showing how electrons may slip about between the atoms of a metal without being perturbed by them, but they still cannot altogether be sure why this happens in some metals and not in others.

A metal, even in the form of a wire, must be looked on as a collection of rather small crystals, in which the metal atoms are arranged in regular rows and planes, the arrangement being called a lattice. The atoms exert forces on each other, attracting or repelling each other according to their distance apart, and thus keeping each other in place. Because of thermal motion they vibrate about their true lattice position, more if warm, less if cold. Most of the electrons belonging to these atoms are bound closely to them just as they are bound to each other, but a few, amounting perhaps to one per atom, are free. They can easily move from one atom to another, particularly if the latter is deficient in electrons.

Quantum Theory

Since about 1900 a succession of great physicists have invented a completely novel way of thinking about atoms, electrons and light of all wavelengths, called quantum theory or wave mechanics. They have shown that atoms and electrons cannot acquire energies of any value, but only of certain values differing by finite amounts. The smallest of these amounts was originally called a quantum, and all differences had to be an integral multiple of it. Quantum theory has enabled people to make a consistent account of nearly all the rather strange things about atomic physics that have kept on coming to light—the stock example being that electrons sometimes seem to behave like light, and light sometimes seems to behave as if it were made of particles. The few strange things that do not immediately fit into the picture, of which superconductivity is one, seem unlikely to overthrow the quantum theory; they merely seem likely to require it to be extended a little.

No proper account of quantum theory can be developed without a great deal of mathematics and measurement. What can be said is that, but for a quantum theory, we should have no accurate understanding of a long list of important phenomena: radiation from a hot body, spectra, fluorescence, why some metals and compounds make permanent magnets, what is a semi-conductor, and how a transistor should be made.

On the subject of electrical resistance, wave mechanics has shown that a perfect conductor is a conceivable idea. If the atoms did not vibrate at all about their lattice positions, and if the wire were a perfect single crystal, wave mechanics predicts that the free electrons should slip through the lattice as if it were not there. By cooling the wire below $4°K$ we can reduce the atom vibrations nearly to nothing, but we cannot make perfect single crystals because no metal can be purified sufficiently. Consider for example a metal containing one foreign atom in a thousand, and imagine the metal crystal divided into cubes of dimensions ten atoms each way. On average there will be one foreign atom in each cube, so no part of the crystal will be much more than five atoms away from the nearest foreign atom. Because they are the wrong size, foreign atoms distort the crystal in their neighbourhood, and the lattice is no longer perfect enough for the free electrons to slip through unimpeded. Probably a crystal with only one in a million of the wrong sort of atoms would be almost a perfect conductor, if it were perfectly formed and its temperature were less than $4°K$ —but no one has yet made metals of such purity.

However, it can be shown experimentally that the superconductors in the low temperature laboratories are not the same thing as the perfect conductors predicted by elementary wave mechanics. The proof hinges on whether or not a magnetic field can exist inside the metal. Fig. 13.1 shows what happens (a) if a magnet is brought near to an ordinary metal (not iron) and taken away again; (b) if while the magnet is near, the metal is somehow turned into a perfect conductor, and then the magnet is taken away; (c) if while the magnet is near, the metal is turned into a superconductor (by cooling it sufficiently), and then the magnet is taken away. Evidently case (b) is quite different from case (c) so the theoretical physicists must think again.

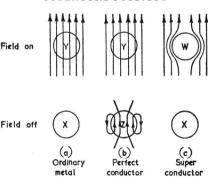

Fig. 13.1. Behaviour in a magnetic field.

In 1957 Bardeen, Cooper and Schrieffer found a possible way of extending wave mechanics so that it might account for superconductivity. They had been working on the fact that the energy needed to destroy the superconductivity of all the electrons in a metal is very small (it is about one hundred-millionth of the energy needed to place the same number of electrons the same distance apart, in a vacuum). This might mean that a quantum of energy had to be shared in some way among the electrons. Now it had already been found necessary to share quanta between the atoms in a crystal, causing their vibrations to be co-operative, like the movements of neighbouring drops in an ocean wave. These co-operative motions of crystal atoms are called phonons, and they account for numerous strange results of measurements of the conduction of heat at low temperatures. In the end, Bardeen, Cooper and Schrieffer introduced the idea of two electrons moving co-operatively, and found that their interaction with the atoms of the crystal lattice produced therein two equal and opposite phonons which cancelled each other out. They proved at least that it is theoretically possible for electrons, moving in twos among the atoms of a crystal, to do so without altering in any way the vibrations of the atoms. The BCS theory fits in very well with an explanation, in terms of an energy gap, why electrons can be superconducting in some metals but not in others.

This account is grossly unfair, because of its simplicity, to all the scientists who have put in a lot of hard thinking and equally hard experimental work, with the specific object of accounting for

superconductivity. The situation is reminiscent of an indefatig-
able sheepdog at work in an exponentially increasing flock of
sheep. For over fifty years since the discovery by Kamerlingh
Onnes, theory has been chasing hard after a growing flock of
experimental results (we shall come across some of them in the
next few pages). Perhaps it is now on the point of rounding nearly
all of them up.

Demonstrations of Superconductivity

In their expansive moments, physicists sometimes work out
experiments which they use to demonstrate as convincingly and
visually as possible that superconductivity really happens. To show
that a piece of wire, buried somewhere in the depth of masses of
equipment, has zero resistance, falls rather flat in a lecture or in
front of a television audience. All they can see is a voltmeter
whose pointer falls steadily from a reading of perhaps 100 divi-
sions to 1 division as the wire cools down, and then rather suddenly drops from 1 division to zero. The audience knows only too
well that if the experiment were going wrong the lecturer could
achieve the same result by quietly undoing a wire from a terminal
at the back of the voltmeter.

However, there are better ways if the audience will accept the
fact that a wire carrying a current must always produce a magnetic
field. In particular, a current in a wire or a coil of any shape will
deflect a compass needle. Secondly, if a magnetic search coil is
twisted in a magnetic field a ballistic galvanometer attached to it
will show a sudden deflection. In one of the earliest public dem-
onstrations of superconductivity, a single closed ring was made of
lead wire, lead being a metal which is superconducting below
$7°K$. The ring was placed in a Dewar flask between the coils of an
electromagnet, and was cooled by immersing it in liquid helium.
When the current of the electromagnet was switched off and the
whole thing taken away, it was found that there was still a "magnet" inside the flask of helium—namely the lead wire which now
had a strong current flowing round it. Compass needles were de-
flected and a ballistic galvanometer gave strong kicks when a
search coil was suitably manipulated. All this happened in Leiden,
but the Dewar flask was now flown to London in one of the ram-
shackle aeroplanes of that epoch, and delivered to the Royal
Institution in Albemarle St. Here a large audience waited in the

lecture theatre, who were shown first that there was still liquid helium in the Dewar so that the lead ought to be still superconducting and still carrying the current. Next they were shown that there was indeed a "magnet" there. Finally the helium was allowed to evaporate and, suddenly, it was found that the "magnet" had gone. When the contents of the Dewar were revealed, nothing was to be found but a rough and ready ring of lead wire. This wire must have been carrying a large current all the time it was at 4°K.

Any metal in the superconducting state excludes from itself all magnetic lines of force, in the way shown in Fig. 13.1. If a 2-in. disc of lead is made into the shape of a shallow dish, and a small steel magnet is laid on it, and both are cooled in liquid helium, the magnet will rise half an inch from the dish and float gently over it like a magic fish. This striking demonstration can be performed before small audiences, who can all see what is happening, provided that a Dewar vessel is used which has unsilvered sides. While the dish is in its normal state, lines of force from the magnet pass through it virtually unchanged. When it becomes superconducting, the lines of force must somehow all find room above the dish. They take the same configuration as if there were a second magnet, like the first, but just below the dish. The real magnet and its image repel each other and they separate until the force between them is just equal to the weight of the magnet.

A similar demonstration can be shown, with the lead as the floating material, if lead foil is wrapped round a balsa-wood ball, and cooled in liquid helium. A circular magnet, the sort used as a focussing magnet for a television tube, can now be pulled up round the outside of the liquid helium vessel. The lines of force make a nest round the lead-coated ball, and the ball is carried up by the magnet, out of the liquid helium into the helium vapour above it. Only when the ball reaches a height at which the temperature of the vapour is over 7°K does it fall, and then it may be caught in a second nest, right in the middle of the ring magnet. When lifted a second time into the over 7°K region, it falls to the bottom of the vessel.

Much of the serious work on superconductors has been concerned with their behaviour in magnetic fields. An electromagnet is always used to produce the magnetic fields, consisting simply of a coil containing a large number of turns of copper wire. The coil is raised into position round the outside of the glass Dewar which contains the liquid nitrogen which prevents too much heat from flowing into the Dewar which contains the liquid helium and the metal specimen. The coil is of course horizontal, i.e. its axis is vertical, and the specimen is as nearly as possible at the centre of the coil. Now by passing different direct currents through the coil, magnetic fields of different strengths can be produced round the specimen.

The first result shown by such an apparatus is that for any superconducting specimen there is a critical magnetic field strength. When the current in the coil is increased above the value necessary to produce the critical field, the specimen quite suddenly ceases to be superconducting. This can be shown in various ways: its resistance can be measured, or the presence of a magnetic field within it can be detected. The critical field of a superconducting material is always the same if the temperature is the same, but as the temperature is lowered the critical field becomes larger. However, even if the temperature is lowered nearly to absolute zero, the critical field never becomes disproportionately large. In fact, superconductivity can always be destroyed by a sufficiently large magnetic field, and it will always return when the field is diminished below the critical value.

Cryotrons and Computers

Consider a short length of fine tin wire, encircled by a loop of lead wire, both at a temperature of $3 \cdot 5°K$. At this temperature both metals are superconductors. Now if a large enough current is passed round the lead wire to make a field of 320 gauss, the tin wire will immediately become a normal conductor and have an electrical resistance. This means that by alternately switching on and off a current through the lead wire, the tin can be "switched" alternately normal and superconducting.

Any device using two superconductors in this way is called a cryotron. It is potentially of great value in building computers. To make a modern computer we require tens or hundreds of thousands of identical devices, each of which can be put into one of two states by an electric current. The ability of a computer to do arithmetic at high speed depends on the way these devices are interconnected so that the state of each one depends on the states of others connected to it. It ought to be possible to make tin-lead cryotrons surprisingly cheaply in very large numbers, with most of their interconnections already built-in, in the form of lead connecting strips. A block containing a million cryotrons would be quite small, perhaps a 4-in. cube, with perhaps 2,000 wires coming out of it. There are technical difficulties, naturally, and determined efforts are being made to overcome them. The cost of keeping the heart of the computer at less than 4°K is small compared with the hundred thousand pounds or more needed to make it. The main technical difficulty is to find a way of making very large numbers of cryotrons, together in one process, all having identical properties.

High-field Superconductors and Power Stations

Associated with the critical field which destroys the super-conductivity of a wire, it is an unfortunate fact that every super-conducting wire has a critical current, more than which it cannot carry without losing its superconductivity. Every wire carrying a current has a magnetic field round it, proportional to the strength of current. The lines of force are in circles round the wire, and they are under a mutual pressure tending to make the circles smaller. If the pressure is great enough near to the surface of a superconducting wire, the lines of force will penetrate the wire and destroy its superconductivity. The practical disadvantage of this is apparent when we try to make powerful magnetic fields by passing a current through a coil of superconducting wire.

The unit of magnetic induction is called the gauss and it is measured by the force on a wire carrying an electric current when it is placed in the magnetic field. The earth has a magnetic field which differs from place to place, but whose value in Britain is near to 0·2 gauss. A powerful electromagnet, consisting of copper coils wound round a soft iron core, the whole weighing about half a ton, can produce a field in the air gap between two iron pole pieces a few inches apart of up to 10,000 gauss.

Ideally, no energy ought to be required for maintaining any magnetic field—after all, a permanent magnet stays magnetized without consuming any energy. In fact, very high energies are required for fields in excess of 20 kilogauss because they have to be produced by electric currents in solenoids, with no help from an iron core, and even with the thickest practicable copper wind-ing the electrical resistance is crucial. The joule heat (current × voltage × time) generated in this resistance has to be carried to

D.O.C.—5*

waste by cooling water, and this is where the power goes. To maintain a field of 100 kilogauss in a coil of 1 metre radius, using water-cooled copper windings, takes 100 megawatts which is a tenth of the output of a large power station. Obviously most of this power could be saved if such large fields could be generated with superconducting coils.

Until a few years ago, all known superconductors were "quenched" in fields of less than 1 kilogauss. However, among the almost infinite number of alloys that are possible, some very unusual ones have recently been found. For instance the metal compound containing 3 atoms of niobium to every 1 atom of tin, Nb_3Sn is a superconductor in fields of 80 kilogauss. An alloy of vanadium and gallium is superconducting even in 300 kilogauss. It has been calculated that less than 100 kilowatts is needed to maintain a one metre diameter superconducting magnet of 100 kilogauss, including the energy for liquefying the requisite helium; this is only one thousandth of the power needed for the same magnet using copper at room temperature.

The most attractive immediate use of cheap high magnetic fields is for magnetohydrodynamic (MHD) power generation. Coal is burnt in compressed air in a furnace at 5,300°F and the ionized gaseous products of combustion pass at high speed across the magnetic field. This sets up a potential difference across the duct carrying the gas, and power is extracted by electrodes placed at the sides of the duct. Such a system could be designed with a generating efficiency of 60 per cent, that is $1\frac{1}{2}$ times better than the best steam power station. The reason for the higher efficiency is the higher temperature in the working section of the duct, much higher than any turbine blades could withstand.

In the future, a second use of high magnetic fields will be for containing the plasmas needed for thermonuclear fusion. There are other uses for making very short radio waves of about 1 mm wavelength, and for masers, infra-red detectors and numerous research purposes.

The usual time to develop prototype machines so completely novel as superconducting magnets is from five to ten years, so by 1970 we can hope for some spectacular news. The same date might apply to the cryotron computers previously mentioned. "Just fancy," we shall be saying "for 60 years superconductivity has been a white elephant, and now it has started to pay dividends."

Chapter Fourteen

LIQUID HELIUM

THE HELIUM ATOM is particularly simple, stable and symmetrical. Its nucleus contains two of each kind of nuclear particle, namely protons (mass one, charge $+1$) and neutrons (mass one, charge 0). (Two, three or four nearly equal marbles can be arranged so that each touches every other member of the group, it will be noticed, but no larger number than four.) Outside the nucleus of helium, there are two electrons, and these are said to "fill the innermost shell". It has long been known from the X-rays produced by different atoms that no more than two electrons can stay so close to the nucleus as these are. The force needed to pull one of the electrons away from the atom is its charge multiplied by 24·56 volts, much more than is needed for any other kind of atom.

Associated with the last fact is another fact, that two or more complete atoms of helium exert very little force on each other, so we can expect liquid helium to have a low boiling point. Raising the temperature of liquid helium to a mere 4·2°K gives the atoms sufficient thermal motion for them to separate from each other, in other words for them to evaporate.

We might therefore expect the helium atom to be the nearest approximation to the hard sphere of classical theory, and liquid helium to be worth studying as if it were the prototype of all other liquids. (Scientists will admit that they understand liquids far less completely than solids or gases.) In actual fact the behaviour of liquid helium is so remarkable that it is well worth studying as the exception, rather than the prototype. The reason for its behaviour is connected with quantum effects which are most easy to detect at the lowest temperatures.

Superfluidity

The natural way to cool liquid helium below its normal boiling point is by pumping the vapour. When the pump is connected to the vessel containing liquid helium, fast boiling occurs as usual, with plenty of bubbles of helium gas rising from the interior of the liquid and rushing up to the surface. Suddenly, when the thermometer indicates 2·18°K, the bubbles stop completely, but the boiling goes on and after a slight hesitation the temperature drops further and the liquid level also continues to drop. The temperature 2·18°K is the famous lambda point; it was thus named because of the resemblance of a plotted set of observations to the Greek small letter lambda (λ). Cessation of bubbling is an absolutely reliable indicator that this temperature has been reached, and the lambda point is regularly used to check thermometers during an experiment.

Above 2·18°K helium is much like other liquids; below, it is as different as superconductors are different from other metals. The most remarkable property is its superfluidity, which was first demonstrated in Cambridge in 1938. Fig. 14.1 represents a

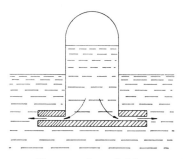

Fig. 14.1. Superfluidity.

pair of optically flat plates pressed so close together that the gap is less than one thousandth of a millimetre. The upper plate has a hole in it over which is sealed a short glass tube. At room temperature the two plates have to be separated by sliding, they are so well wrung together. If an ordinary liquid is put inside it will not escape at all. If liquid helium is put inside it does not escape unless the temperature is below the lambda point, and then it flows through the gap with a velocity of many centimetres per second. The property which inhibits the flow of fluids, a sort of internal friction, is called viscosity, and this liquid apparently has no viscosity at all.

A good way to describe many of the properties of this liquid is to regard it as a mixture of two fluids, a normal fluid *n*, and a superfluid *s*, the latter having no fluid friction, zero viscosity. This is sufficient to account for the experiment illustrated in Fig. Atkins 1a, because *s* slips through the gap between the glass plates, temporarily increasing the relative concentration of *s* outside the glass tube and decreasing it inside. Down to 2·18°K, of course, liquid helium is all *n*, but measurements show that as the temperature is lowered further, it contains an increasing proportion of *s*, until around 1°K it is nearly all *s*.

A neat way to measure the proportions of *n* and *s* at any temperature is to make a pile of light discs, as in Fig. 14.2. The gaps between the discs should be not more than 0.21 mm. Now they are suspended in normal helium at the bottom of a metal strip or wire, and the top of the wire is given a sudden twist through about a right angle. Any weight at the bottom of such a wire will oscillate, not like a pendulum but torsionally. The time of a complete oscillation (the period of

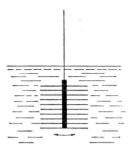

Fig. 14.2. Torsion pendulum in liquid helium.

oscillation) depends on the stiffness of the wire, and on the mass and shape of the weight combined in a formula known as its moment of inertia. Now comes the reason for the gap of 0·21 mm, because any *n* helium within such a narrow gap stays in position relative to the plates—that is to say it oscillates with them and contributes to their moment of inertia. But when the helium is cooled below the lambda point, part of it turns to *s*, and this part will not oscillate with the plates however close they are. Thus by measuring periods of oscillation in helium of differing temperatures, it is easy to calculate what proportion is *n* or *s*.

Ordinary mixtures of two intersoluble fluids, like water and alcohol, are very difficult to separate. If they were not, we should all be converting our beer and cider into something stronger. However, helium *n* and *s* separate quite easily, for the last two illustrations show them, not separating perhaps, but going different ways. A spectacular way of producing a high concentration of helium *s* is with the dipping beaker of Fig. 14.3. A small glass tube or beaker is lowered into liquid helium *n* and *s* without going under, as in (*a*). Immediately an invisible film of *s* creeps up the outside of the beaker and down the inside filling it up quite quickly until the helium is the same level inside as out. If the beaker is raised a little as in (*b*) the helium flows the other way, and in (*c*) the drops can actually be seen forming and dripping off the bottom. This experiment is no trick, and the thickness of

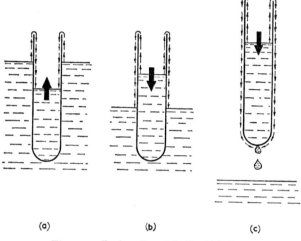

(a)   (b)   (c)

Fig. 14.3. Beaker dipped in liquid helium.

the creeping film can be measured by light polarization and other means to be about 3 millionths of a cm at a height of 1 cm above the bulk liquid. It is false, however, to imagine that the liquid collected in the dipping beaker (*a*) is pure *s*, because by the time it has got there it will have nearly completed its reconversion to the mixture of *s* and *n* appropriate to its temperature. Undoubtedly the simplest way to obtain nearly pure *s* is to cool the helium below 1°K.

The readiness of the two heliums to move independently leads to other surprising happenings when there is a temperature gradient in the liquid, and one part of it is heated, say, 0·1° above the liquid 1 cm away. The warm place attracts helium *s* so rapidly that a pressure of helium builds up there. In Fig. 14.4 the bent tube at the bottom contains a black powder such as emery, through which *s* can pass easily but not *n*. The powder can be warmed sufficiently by shining a light on it. Being a much better absorber of light and heat energy than the transparent liquid

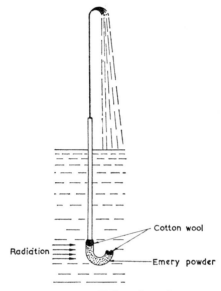

Fig. 14.4. Helium fountain.

helium it is immersed in, it becomes perhaps 0·1° warmer than the liquid, which should be well below the lambda point for the experiment to work. Helium *s* rushes into the bent tube so quickly that it carries on up into the capillary tube and out at the top. This is a continuous process, forming a fountain which can be as much as a foot high.

Naturally there is energy in such a jet of liquid helium, and three or four jets can be made to drive a jet propelled spider, as illustrated in Fig. 14.5.

In ordinary circumstances, in a vessel containing liquid helium *n* and *s*, temperature differences simply cannot exist. As soon as one part becomes the least bit warmer than its surroundings *s* rushes towards it and *n* flows away from it, lowering the temperature of that region until all is steady once more. All this happens

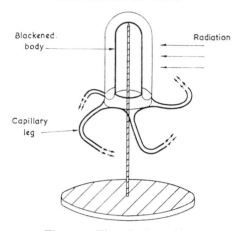

Fig. 14.5. The spinning spider.

without any visible disturbance, because n and s pass through each other without any viscosity. As a result, superfluid helium is the most perfect "conductor" of heat known; however it is as well to notice that heat is not really transferred by conduction, but by a sort of frictionless convection which can take heat in any direction and not merely upwards as in ordinary convection.

Second Sound

The ability of s and n to slide freely through each other was seen in 1940 to render possible a completely novel kind of wave motion, initiated by periodically varying temperature. If a large group of s atoms could be moved to one side and then back again, in an oscillatory movement, neighbouring n atoms would have to move alternately into and out of the region first vacated by s atoms. From this centre of activity there would spread out into the rest of the helium an oscillatory motion of s atoms and a counter motion of n atoms. There would be nothing visible, of course, because the combined density of n and s would not be changed anywhere, but this motion could be detected in other ways. For example, a small resistance thermometer would show oscillations of temperature, because s atoms would never communicate their motion to it, whereas the vibratory thermal motions of n atoms would be communicated to it in the ordinary way. Therefore, whenever the thermometer wire was surrounded by an excess of *s* atoms it would register a diminished temperature, and whenever it was surrounded by an excess of *n* atoms it would show an elevated temperature.

Fig. 14.6 represents the apparatus which first demonstrated the effect, in 1944. Notice that it is a genuine wave motion, and the waves (of high and low *s* concentration, accompanied by

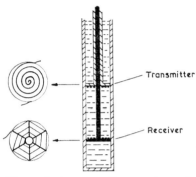

Fig. 14.6. Apparatus for second sound.

low and high *n* concentration) must spread out from the centre with a definite velocity. The same thing happens if one end of a long rope is waved rhythmically or if a stick is dabbled in a pond. The nearest type of wave motion to these new temperature waves was thought to be ordinary sound. Air-borne sound originates from the centre where the air pressure is made to oscillate above and below its average value, and air density does the same. This is somewhat analogous to the oscillations in density of helium *s* or *n*, and so the temperature waves acquired the name of "second sound". Some scientists have found this name rather regrettable, because they are also very much interested in the transmission of ordinary "first" sound by solids and liquids, and this has little to do with density oscillations but a lot do to with phonons. However, the name of second sound has stuck for keeps, apparently.

There are no spectacular experiments to demonstrate second sound, although there is one which might be called intellectually spectacular. If the waves are allowed to reach the surface of liquid helium in the bath, the temperature there will oscillate; when it is high helium will evaporate faster than average, and when it is low slower than average. (Remember that to maintain such low temperatures the helium has to be kept evaporating all the time, to compensate for the heat leaking in.) These fluctuations in rate of evaporation can be directly observed as *first* sound, since they produce fluctuations in gas pressure and these are, in fact, first sound.

Theoretical physicists have produced numerous calculations about both first and second sound in superfluid helium, concerning their velocity and attenuation. The velocity of second sound is about one tenth that of ordinary sound, but both depend on the temperature and pressure in different ways. Theory has turned out to be satisfactory up to a point, but it has to rely on the two-fluid model with which quantum physicists are still grappling. Two other modes of wave propagation, which are neither first nor second sound but a little of each, have been predicted and found. One occurs when the experimenter tries to propagate first sound in very narrow channels, between two optically flat plates such as those mentioned much earlier in the chapter. The other occurs when second sound is propagated along the extremely thin films of superfluid helium which have been referred to as creeping films. Both are difficult experiments, but they are just within the capabilities of modern equipment and techniques.

Task for theoreticians

Any good theory about liquid helium must begin by giving a plausible reason why a superfluid component forms at temperatures below the lambda point, increasing in proportion as the temperature drops further, until at the absolute zero all the liquid is superfluid. After that, the theory must correctly predict the shape of curves, such as the variation with temperature of specific heat, viscosity and fraction of the superfluid component. An intriguing and partly successful approach was made in 1938, by pretending that liquid helium was like a gas. Because the helium atom contains an even number of fundamental particles (2 protons, 2 neutrons and 2 electrons) a particular set of equations ought to determine how many of the atoms may have each of the quantized energy values when the gas is very cold. The equations are called Bose-Einstein statistics, after Bose and the great Albert Einstein who first introduced them. With just these

equations from an epoch some 20 years earlier, it was found that
ordinarily none of the atoms should have zero energy, but that
below a certain temperature which could be calculated to be
3·13°K a proportion of atoms (increasing as the temperature fell
still lower) must have zero energy. These zero-energy atoms
could be expected to behave just like the s atoms of helium. The
calculated lambda point of 3·13°K was creditably near the actual
lambda point of 2·18°K, and the difference might reasonably be
due to the assumption that liquid helium was a gas although its
atoms come rather too close together for a gas. Unfortunately
there turned out to be other difficulties connected with the pre-
diction of shapes of curves, and no one has yet circumvented
them by any extension of this particular theory.

A second type of theory begins with the very different thought
that liquid helium is like a solid. As in crystals its atoms can perform co-operative thermal vibrations, called phonons, and these
are restricted to definite quantized energy levels. So far it is like
the beginning of an approach to theories of the superconductivity
of metals, but phonons in liquid helium lose their importance as
the temperature is increased from 0°K. A new type of co-operative motion, also quantized, comes into play. This is a sort of
eddy, or stirring motion, and it is obviously possible in liquids
but not in crystals. Quantized stirring movements were frankly
postulated in the hope of explaining superfluidity, and were called
rotons. No basis could at first be found on which a lambda point
could be computed, but some good forecasts were made of how
the expansion coefficient of liquid helium ought to change with
temperatures between 0·8°K and 1·4°K. Then, by some plausible
mathematical short cuts, to "guess" the solutions of equations
which cannot be solved even by modern computers, the begin-
nings of an explanation of the lambda transition were found.
Whether this is the right approach or a blind alley remains to be
seen, because people are still working on this kind of theory.

Helium Three (He³)

If we include the transuranium elements which have recently
been made in nuclear reactors, there are 102 elements on this
earth. Each element has a different number of electrons attached
to its nucleus, beginning with one electron for hydrogen, two for
helium, and so on right up to 102 for Nobelium. In fact it is

sometimes convenient to refer to an element not by its name but by its number, so that carbon, nitrogen and oxygen, for example, are respectively called element 6, 7 and 8 because these are the numbers of electrons per atom of these elements. The nucleus of of an element has to have as many positive units of charge as there are electrons, and it possesses this number of protons, each of unit mass and unit positive charge. Thus the hydrogen nucleus has one proton, the oxygen nucleus eight, etc. In addition the nucleus must, apparently, have a reasonable number of neutrons, of unit mass and charge zero. A "reasonable number" turns out in practice to be about the same as the number of protons in an element, though rather more for elements number 20 and over. However, for every element which we have, several numbers of neutrons can exist in its nucleus, up to as many as five more or five less than the most common number.

This not very astonishing fact went unnoticed for a great many years, because the properties of the different elements were studied by chemists, and chemical reactions do not disturb the nucleus of any element. It was first seen to be likely in 1912, when physicists had started to drive streams of atoms about in electric and magnetic fields. When the discovery had been fully checked, the different types of atom constituting an element were called the isotopes of that element. Notice that the isotopes of any element have different numbers of neutrons in the nucleus, but the same number of protons in the nucleus, the same number of electrons round it, and the same chemical properties. Isotopes cannot be separated chemically from each other, and physical methods such as fractional distillation, diffusion and the like are extremely slow and costly. No one knows why the isotopes of each element are always found in the same proportions in all parts of the world, but they are, with a few easily explained exceptions.

Helium, by the way, is one of the exceptions. It has two stable isotopes: helium four, He^4, which has four particles in its nucleus, two protons and two neutrons, and He^3 whose nucleus has two protons and one neutron. In the helium found in oil wells, 14 atoms in every hundred million are He^3 and the rest are He^4; in the helium in the atmosphere the proportion is 120 atoms in 100 million. It is believed that well helium was created by the decay of radioactive elements, but that atmospheric helium came from the sun when the earth was made.

Even the physical properties of isotopes are not usually very different from each other, but physicists longed to study pure He^3, because they thought it would have a lower boiling point than normal helium which to all intents and purposes is He^4. It might even go solid on pumping the vapour, unlike He^4 but like all the other liquids known. It is magnetic, whereas He^4 is non-magnetic. But above all, they wanted to make liquid He^3 because its nucleus contains an odd number of particles. The quantum equations of Bose and Einstein are not applicable to such substances, and in their place some very different equations by Fermi and Dirac should be used. Although the Bose-Einstein equations do not appear to predict all the behaviour of liquid He^4, they are very definite about the lambda transition and the superfluid phase; but Fermi-Dirac predict no such phenomenon.

Almost pure He^3 began to be produced in nuclear reactors in the late 1940s. The working particles of reactors are enormous numbers of neutrons, and these were used to bombard lithium (atomic number, 3) to form tritium (H^3, an unstable isotope of hydrogen) and He^4. The tritium was separated from the He^4, not chemically though this would be possible, but by the physical process of diffusion through red hot palladium (this metal lets hydrogen and its isotopes pass through, but no other gas). The pure tritium slowly decays to give He^3 and an electron.

Helium three was successfully liquefied at a temperature of $3 \cdot 19^\circ K$ making it the most "permanent" of all gases. This temperature was predicted a year previously, within a fifth of a degree, by a simple modification to the laws of a perfect gas which allowed for quantum effects. The vapour pressure was found to be much higher than that of He^4 right down to $0 \cdot 1^\circ K$, which meant that by pumping the vapour of He^3 liquid baths could be obtained down to $0 \cdot 1^\circ K$ compared with the previous limit of $0 \cdot 85^\circ K$. For quite a number of experiments such baths are needed, and although He^3 is virtually priceless it is actually used today as a cryogenic fluid.

The next measurements on liquid He^3 were designed to find whether it had a lambda transition. Its specific heat was measured at all temperatures down to $0 \cdot 2^\circ K$, that is the heat needed to raise a given mass by a given small temperature. Whereas He^4 has quite high specific heats between $2 \cdot 0$ and $2 \cdot 3^\circ K$ (the lambda temperature) He^3 has no such anomaly. None of the associated phenomena, creeping films, superfluidity, mechanocaloric and thermo-mechanical effects, or second sound are to be found either. So it seems very unlikely that there can be a superfluid He^3.

All the same, theoretical physicists find much to occupy them over He^3. Its specific heat below $1°K$ shows strong evidence that its atoms are getting their magnetic spins into line, because extra heat is needed to warm up the liquid and get them out of line. Below about $0.1°K$ the liquid will probably behave like an ideal Fermi-Dirac gas and its specific heat will fall steeply to zero. Whatever small energy its atoms will have, they will rarely be able to pass on or receive from others. Now ordinary sound, whether it is transmitted in a solid, gas or liquid, depends upon energy being passed on rapidly from atom to atom. So the theoreticians believe that no ordinary sound will pass through He^3 when very near to the absolute zero of temperature. They believe, however, that another kind of vibration, which they call zero sound, can pass through He^3 at a velocity nearly twice that of ordinary first sound. The experimentalists have not yet verified these predictions.

Chapter Fifteen

PHONONS AND THE
CONDUCTION OF HEAT

IN THE KINETIC THEORY of gases, in Chapter Two, heat was identified with the energy of gas molecules. They had kinetic energy $\frac{1}{2}mv^2$, and if they consisted of two or more atoms they also had energies of vibration and rotation. If the molecules in one region of a gas are heated up, their energies increase and they dash away and collide with less energetic molecules, transferring some of their surplus energy. As the newly energized molecules dash off in their turn, the extra energy spreads further and further afield. Observations show that temperatures rise, and heat is indeed being conducted from the original hot spot to the colder regions of the gas.

Something rather similar happens during the conduction of heat by metals, which are well known to be better conductors than non-metals. They owe this facility to their abundance of free electrons, normally thought of as carriers of electricity. If one end of a bar of metal is heated to a higher temperature than the other, the electrons in the hotter end acquire higher velocities than those in the cooler end. Since the free electrons in a metal belong to the solid as a whole and not to individual atoms, the energetic electrons can flow to the cold end and the less energetic electrons to the hot end. Thus the surplus kinetic energy is transferred to the cold end, where it is absorbed by the atoms whenever a fast electron collides with them, and the temperature rises there.

The heat flow in metals turns out to be greatest when the electrons move farthest without being diverted by an atom. It is sometimes claimed that, if an energetic electron could move throughout a metal specimen without being scattered or losing its energy, as in the perfect conductor discussed in Chapter Eleven, the metal would have infinite thermal conductivity. This is not quite true. Unless there is some interaction between electrons and the atoms in the crystal lattice, the electrons can play no rôle in carrying energy from one part of the lattice to another. However, a very occasional collision between electrons and lattice atoms is sufficient to put them in temperature equilibrium with each other, so it can be said that a nearly perfect conductor of electric current would have a very high thermal conductivity. In superconductors, which we saw were different from perfect conductors, the super-conducting electrons play no part in transferring heat energy, and they reduce the number of available normal free electrons. Hence superconductors generally have a lower conductivity for heat than the same metal in the normal state.

Imperfections in the crystal lattice of a metal, the obstacles to electrons in their otherwise free motion, are of three kinds. First there are the impurity atoms of different material which can only fit into place by distorting the neighbouring atoms from their true lattice position. Then there are strains and dislocations in the crystal, caused by bending, hammering, wire drawing and so on; and it must be remembered that both the outside surface and the interface between different crystal regions are places where atoms are not symmetrically surrounded by their kind, so these too are places of strain. Finally there are the vibrations of the atoms about their lattice positions, the restless thermal motion which only stops at absolute zero. All these "imperfections" have the effect of putting atoms into unexpected positions where they are likely to obstruct electrons. Hence imperfections reduce the conduction of heat by free electrons.

A good metallic conductor of electricity is a good conductor of heat, as might be expected. Silver and copper are the best conductors of both electricity and heat.

Lowering the temperature of a metal lowers the size of one of its imperfections—the atomic vibrations—and therefore increases the electrical conductivity by lengthening the paths of electrons between successive lattice collisions. But it also lowers the velocity of the electrons, and the energy they carry, and this effect, by itself, would *reduce* the rate at which electrons transfer heat. When allowance is made for their longer path lengths, however, it turns out that they carry the same total of energy as before. The result is, then, that whereas electrons are better conductors of electricity in metals at lower temperatures, they are neither better nor worse conductors of heat.

Phonons

In materials where there are hardly any free electrons, i.e. in insulators, the electrical conductivity is extremely low. The conductivity for heat, also, is lower than in metals, but not by any means extremely low. The reason is that in insulators there is considerable conduction of heat by phonons, while phonons are useless for the conduction of electricity.

We have seen that phonons are quanta of sound waves, produced when even a single atom is disturbed from its true lattice position. If one atom is displaced, its neighbours which are trying to hold it in place are displaced too, and as they spring back a disturbance spreads right through the lattice like a sound wave. In books about quantum theory there are descriptions of photons, which are bundles of light waves travelling through space or through matter such as glass with the velocity of light. Photons do not change at all until they collide with matter or, occasionally, with each other, and then they change suddenly into some other form of energy. Phonons are similar, but they are bundles of sound waves. Their wavelengths are very short and their frequencies are very high, because they are the frequencies of vibrations of atoms in the strong interatomic force fields inside a crystal. They are more than thirty octaves above the top end of a piano. Phonons keep their idenity, like photons, until they collide with each other, or with atoms or electrons. Unlike photons, they cannot travel through gases or empty space.

We have seen that phonons are produced when electrons collide with the lattice atoms of a metal; but that they are not produced by superconducting electrons. They are also important in the superfluidity of liquid helium. But their outstanding importance is in the general conduction of heat in solids, and the best way of studying them is at low temperatures, when there are not too many of them and they are not too strong. At high temperatures they collide with each other and turn into other phonons almost before they have started off; but at low temperatures a phonon may keep its identity and travel the relatively enormous distance of a millimetre or so before it collides and changes.

Some very interesting measurements have been made on the thermal conductivity of non-metals like rocksalt and beryl, in the form of crystals as near perfect as possible. At low enough temperatures the thermal conductivity increases spectacularly. In one specimen it was found to reach 400 times the thermal conductivity of the same crystal at room temperature. This can make them into better conductors of heat than metals. Lithium fluoride at 20°K can have five times the thermal conductivity of silver at any temperature. The old Eskimo warning, not to handle any metal at subzero temperatures, is sound enough as far as it goes. The bare hand, in contact with cold metal, loses heat so fast that tissue damage is inevitable—and this is made worse by the freezing of the hand on to the metal. To handle a stick or other insulator, on the contrary, is fairly safe, even if it has just been dipped in liquid helium. What the Eskimos probably do not know, however, is that their warning should be even more stringent in the case of crystalline insulators than for metals. If someone were to offer you a large crystal of rocksalt (common salt) which he had just taken out of liquid hydrogen, for example, you must refuse to touch it. Luckily such a gift is unlikely to come your way, and if it were held out to you, it would be quite frightening enough to make you keep away. It would be dripping with liquid air, and surrounded with clouds of "steam" condensing from the atmosphere. So quickly would it be absorbing heat from the air around it that it would reach a safe temperature before you could summon the necessary courage to touch it, anyhow.

On a more scientific level, experiments have been made to demonstrate the nature of phonons, if indeed these are the real and proper conductors of heat in non-metals. Theory shows that, as the temperature of a crystal is lowered, phonons will travel greater and greater distances before colliding or interacting with other phonons. In a small enough crystal specimen, at low enough temperature, they will therefore collide with the boundary of the specimen more frequently than with each other. The experiment which suggests itself is to make a nearly perfect single crystal of a suitable substance, cut from it a thin rod and a thick rod, and measure the thermal conductivities of the two rods. Sure enough, below 20°K, the thin rod has a lower thermal conductivity than the thick rod. In case this does not seem remarkable, remember that a thick and a thin copper wire, for example, have equal conductivity because the units of conductivity are chosen to take care of differences in cross section.

Metal crystals owe some of their heat conducting powers to

phonons, but in the ordinary way the contribution of phonons is swamped by the much more efficient electrons. Even in temperature regions where non-metals achieve higher conductivities than ordinary copper and silver, it is found that the phonon conductivity of metals is swamped by their electron conductivity. However, phonon conductivity has been detected in alloys, whose imperfections are more obstructive to the passage of electrons than to phonons. Phonon conductivity is easiest of all to demonstrate in superconductors where, as we have seen, the superconducting electrons make no contribution to the transfer of heat.

Imperfections

Unfortunately, all measurements of thermal conductivity at low temperatures are marred by imperfections, and these cannot be controlled very well. No one can make a series of crystal specimens, metal or non-metal, all of which have identical imperfections. The obstruction which imperfections cause to the passage of electrons, noted earlier in this chapter, has a counterpart in their obstruction to the passage of phonons. All three types of imperfection, namely impurities, crystal dislocations, and atom vibrations, scatter phonons in the same general way as they scatter electrons—though in detail the actions are different.

Impurity atoms are tremendous obstacles to phonons. Fig. 15.1 shows the curve of thermal conductivity plotted against temperature for three sodium chloride crystals, as measured at Cornell University. The scales along the axes are logarithmic, so it is better to read the numbers attached to the lines than to judge distances by eye. The best specimen, at 10°K, had a thermal conductivity of 1,000, compared with 50 for the poorest specimen, and the differences were even greater below this temperature. Yet the poorest specimen was prepared from commercially pure sodium chloride; the best was of salt that had been purified very carefully in the laboratory.

Neither physicist nor chemist can make a perfectly pure crystal specimen, more is the pity, and their task is made harder by their having to attach two thermometers to any specimen whose heat conductivity has to be measured. One thing that can be done, however, is to introduce a controlled amount of impurity into a specimen without otherwise disturbing it. If a crystal of lithium fluoride is placed in an X-ray beam of known composition for a

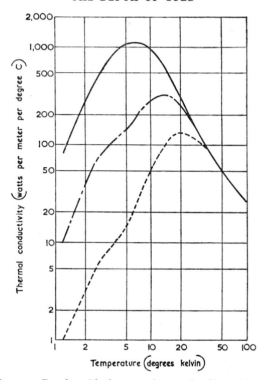

Fig. 15.1. Results with three specimens of sodium chloride.

measured time, impurities of a particular kind known as F-centres are produced and their number can be calculated. An F-centre is a place in the crystal lattice where a fluorine atom has been knocked out by an X-ray, and replaced by an electron. The atoms nearest to an F-centre are subject to electrical and other forces from the electron instead of from a fluorine atom, and are displaced from their true positions. This is the same situation as for any other kind of impurity, though the magnitude of the displacements will be different. Experiments show large changes in heat conductivity when there is even one F-centre for every 100,000 atoms.

Another kind of impurity exists which requires no chemical modification of the material. This is the isotope impurity. Lithium is a mixture of two isotopes, of atomic weights 6 and 7. Only recently, by radiochemical techniques, it has been possible to obtain the two isotopes nearly pure and to mix them in any desired proportions. When they have been made into crystalline lithium fluoride, the thermal conductivity of a fifty-fifty mixture at 30°K is well under half that of either nearly pure isotope. The crystal lattice in which atoms of atomic weight 6 and 7 are distributed at random has a marked overall "imperfection" when compared with the salt made from a single isotope.

Finally we may return to sodium chloride, the subject of Fig. 15.1. The investigation at Cornell seemed to show that the poorer specimens of sodium chloride contained a little oxygen as impurity; so the experimenters deliberately added a known amount of oxygen to the best crystal. They found that one part in 3,000 was enough to reduce its conductivity to that of the poorest. They concluded that this was the concentration of impurity in the poorest specimen, and that the best specimen originally had only one part in 300,000.

We have seen that the conduction of heat in crystals can be explained in terms of electrons (for metals) and phonons (mainly for nonmetals). Electrons are now thoroughly accepted into the scientific menage, and we should be lost without them. Ought we similarly to accept phonons? The balance of evidence is that we ought, but perhaps we should keep them on probation for a few more years yet.

Chapter Sixteen

THE LAST DEGREE

A DEGREE MORE or less does not often make much difference to the human environment, and we rarely object if the temperature of the air in a room suddenly jumps from 20°C to 21°C or back again. However, at very low temperatures a degree can be very important—all the different things that happen to liquid helium happen in a range of less than 4 degrees, and we can quite easily control its temperature, if we want, to within 0·01°C. A better way to see what matters is to consider successively reducing the temperature in degrees absolute by factors of 10. Our normal environmental temperature is a few degrees below 300°K. All the usual phenomena of fog, cloud, ice and snow are familiar to us, because they occur in the range from 300°K to a few degrees below the ice point which is 273°K.

If we try cooling materials from 300°K to 30°K a large number of new and curious things happen. Air turns first to liquid and then to solid. Oxygen and nitrogen become easy to separate. New liquid fuels such as methane and ethylene appear. Ammonia has a range of temperatures in which it is liquid, and solids dissolved in it are ionized, as in water. Liquid oxygen is potentially dangerous as the cause of explosive combustion, and potentially useful as a rocket propellant. All this and much more has been discovered in the last 80 years.

If we cool from 30°K to 3°K the last three gases liquefy and two of them solidify. Metals display the unbelievable property of superconductivity. Various other quantum effects, including the specific heat of electrons, become observable. Studies in this range of temperature have been going on feverishly for the last fifty years and more.

The step from 3°K to 0·3°K was partly made almost as soon as helium was liquefied, but pure liquid helium was not cooled right down to 0·3°K until He^3 was isolated. In this range, helium fails to go solid when being cooled by pumping, instead it must be compressed to over 20 atmospheres pressure. However, the liquid undergoes an extraordinary transition at 2·19°K below which it behaves like a mixture of two liquids, one of which is an entirely new kind now called a superfluid. The isotope He³ fails to show superfluidity. Studies of the colder forms of liquid have been going on for thirty years.

What of the temperature ranges 0·3 to 0·03, 0·03 to 0·003 to 0·0003°K? Are we to expect hitherto unknown phenomena, ten, a hundred or a thousand times as strange as superconductivity and superfluidity? Probably not, because there are no more gases left to liquefy, unless we discover a way of condensing pure neutrons into a liquid. Quantum theory has no suggestion of any more forms of non-classical energy, other that the zero point energy which is enough to keep helium a liquid even at absolute zero. In fact, it is rather surprising that we can take any more energy out of a material whose atomic vibrations are chilled to a temperature of 0·3°K. Very little energy is left, and yet from certain materials we can take enough of that little to cool them right into the coldest of the three ranges listed above.

To understand how it is done, it is necessary to consider the magnetic nature of the electrons in an atom. Any current, going round a coil for example, produces a magnetic field of force. Even a charged solid, like a glass or plastic rod that has been rubbed with a cloth, can be swung round and round to produce a minute magnetic field. When it was found that "stationary" electrons seemed to have a direction in space which could be changed by a magnetic field it seemed simplest to assume that every electron has a magnetic field of its own, and that its charge is spinning at the right speed to produce this field. No one has ever seen a spinning electron or observed its velocity of spin, and the picture of a spinning ball of charge which these words conjure up may be altogether wrong. Indeed all we can measure is the energy needed to convert an electron from one direction or state of spin (which we call $S = -\frac{1}{2}$) to the other, which we call $S = +\frac{1}{2}$. When the electrons are in a magnetic field just these two energy levels are possible, and the energy difference between them is a constant times H, the strength of the magnetic field. When there is no magnetic field other than that of each electron, only one energy level is possible, as if the electron spins are all oriented at random.

Energy Levels

So many mentions of energy levels have been made in this book that it would be best to consider what they mean, first in terms of definite experimental measurement, and then in terms of the simplified model of an atom which is nearly always used by practical physicists. Well then, to measure energy levels we use various forms of spectrometer. A glass prism, showing the rainbow colours of the sun's white light, is the earliest and simplest spectrometer, because it separates mixed light into different wavelengths. A careful examination of the sun's spectrum will show that the smooth merging of colours from blue to red is interrupted by a large number of fine black lines, each of which represents a wavelength of light which started off from the sun but which had its energy used for another purpose while on its way. For instance, two prominent black lines at the blue end of the spectrum are known as the H and K lines of calcium. They have been found to be due to the presence in the outer gases of the sun of atoms of calcium. Not all the calcium atoms in these gases have helped to produce H and K lines; only those which have lost two of their outermost electrons: and of these, only those which have absorbed exactly the right energy from sunlight to move a third of the outermost electrons from a particular low energy level to a higher level. (The upper level is different for H and for K.)

We now know the energy levels not only of calcium in its various states of ionization, but of all elements and of a great many compounds. If radiation passes through a compound of two or more elements, not only the electrons will absorb energy of the exact wavelength needed; the atoms will alter their energy levels in relation to each other. Likewise the atoms in a crystal will absorb energy in order to improve what might be called their energy status, and in this case it does not matter whether the atoms in a crystal are all the same (as in a diamond, which is pure carbon) or different (as in a sapphire which contains aluminium and oxygen).

We know all these energy levels from an immense number of measurements of wavelengths. The sunlight which passes through a prism is separated into a small range of wavelength between 0·4 and 0·8 thousandths of a millimetre. Other wavelengths either fail to pass through the glass of the prism, or fail to reach the ground because of very strong absorption in the earth's atmosphere, or fail to leave the sun. However, we can make radiation of almost any wavelength we need, in the laboratory, and we have instruments for accurately measuring its wavelengths. All such instruments are called spectrometers, if they work anywhere in the range from a hundred-thousandth to ten thousand times the wavelength of visible light. Those working in different ranges of wavelength may look very different, and may employ different techniques of wave separation and measurement, but they all have the same functional purpose—to measure wavelengths. And in most of this enormous range of wavelengths, certainly between one ten-thousandth and ten thousand times the wavelength of light, we can produce fine absorption lines, corresponding to the elevation of atoms or electrons from one energy level to another.

To describe the modern simplified model of an atom, it is best to start with the even simpler model used by Lord Rutherford when he found that atoms consisted of a nucleus surrounded by electrons. In this model it seemed important to explain why the electrons were both attracted by the nucleus and repelled in some way which prevented them from "falling" into the nucleus and losing their identity. The attraction was easy to explain, because the electron is negatively charged and the nucleus is positively charged; the repulsion was thought to be like that which holds planets off from the sun, namely the effect of their momentum round their orbits. This Rutherford model soon became suspect however, for it did not explain spectral absorption lines, and it seemed to require that the electrons should radiate energy away and fall into the nucleus after all. Vestiges of Rutherford's language remain in our present model, for we still speak of orbits, angular momentum, and spin, as if the electrons really circle round the nucleus, spinning as they go. All the same we have to remember that these movements have never been observed or even inferred from observation. Rutherford's words are now convenient labels for different classes of numbers, called quantum numbers.

In the simple modern quantum model, we think of atoms in a molecule or crystal as if they were spheres, capable of rotating and of vibrating about their equilibrium positions. According to rules which fit both the mathematics of quantum mechanics and the measurements of observation, only particular energies of vibration can happen. These energies can only have values $\frac{1}{2}hv_0$, $1\frac{1}{2}hv_0$, $2\frac{1}{2}hv_0$, etc., increasing by hv_0 at a time where h is a universal constant and v_0 is another constant which depends on the mass of the atom and the field of force it is in. This quantization would be accurate if the atom were in an unchangeable field of force like a ball in the middle of a stretched piece of elastic; but in solids and liquids the field of force is entirely due to the nearness of other atoms, and these also can vibrate. The best model for this situation is one which supposes that the atoms vibrate co-operatively (without specifying how they do it), and very many energy levels now replace the few vibrational levels of the free atom in a fixed field. The co-operative modes of vibration we have called phonons, and they ripple to and fro in the crystal with the speed of sound. The most important quality is that there can be single phonons possessing extremely small quanta of energy. If it were not for these, temperature equilibrium would not be possible in cold objects, and the whole idea of temperature would be untenable. If a crystal has n atoms (n being usually a very large number, of course), the modern approach is to think of the energy of the crystal as $\frac{1}{2}nhv_0$ plus a variable number of phonons, whose energies are very small if the temperature is low. Less than $\frac{1}{2}nhv_0$ is impossible, and this is the zero point energy referred to earlier in this chapter.

The function of phonons is the same in our descriptions of liquids as in solids. It is well known, for instance, that when liquid helium is evaporating (because the vapour is being pumped, perhaps), the temperature of the liquid must fall. The phonon description of this phenomenon would be that, in order to escape from the attractive forces of the liquid, any atom must acquire energy, and this it does by absorbing one of the phonons in the liquid. A whole phonon is more than its fair share, so it reduces the phonon density in the liquid it leaves behind, and this is the same thing as making it colder.

A Compressible Liquid

We have seen that pumping helium vapour will only with great difficulty reduce its temperature below $1°K$, and the reason is that although the energy needed to make an atom escape is no larger than at 4°K, there are extremely few phonons of the requisite energy at the lower temperature. However, liquid helium can be squeezed under pressure into about half its normal volume. Other liquids can hardly be squeezed at all, because their zero point energy is not so prominent as that of helium. The effect of squeezing liquid helium is to increase the force field in which every atom vibrates, and thus to increase the energy of each phonon by shortening its wavelength. The temperature therefore rises, but it can be lowered again by surrounding the compressed helium vessel with more helium, boiling under a very low pressure. The state of the helium before and after compression-and-recooling is shown by the first two parts of Fig. 16.1. Each of

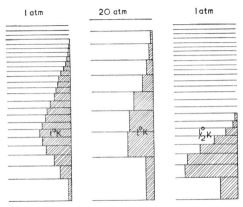

Fig. 16.1. Effect of decompressing liquid helium.

the parallel lines represents a possible energy state for the phonons, and the hatched area immediately above each line is proportional to the number of phonons in that state. On the left the liquid helium is at ordinary pressure, the energy states are close together, and the 4th, 5th and 6th states counting from the bottom are the ones with most phonons, as in the middle diagram. Notice that the general outline of the hatched areas in these two parts of the figure is as nearly as possible the same; meaning that the temperature is the same, in spite of the different energy differences. The final step is to reduce the pressure on the liquid helium back to normal—unsqueezing it. The energy differences close up again, and each phonon stays with its state number. The outline of the hatched areas now looks very different from the other two, and the temperautre is much lower. Very roughly, this is the explanation of cooling by expansion in terms of phonons: it is no better and no worse at higher temperatures, than the explanation in Chapter Six in terms of classical kinetic theory. The reason for presenting it here is the importance of quanta at very low temperatures, and particularly in the magnetic cooling method, which can be explained by the quantum model but not by kinetic theory.

Cooling by the expansion of liquid He^4 and He^3 has little practical value, because a single stage of expansion would not cool specimens below about $\frac{1}{2}°K$. The same objection prohibits any use of the superfluid He^4 by separating it from the normal fluid.

Cooling through Superconductivity

If liquid helium is far from ideal as a "working substance" for further cooling, what about other materials, superconductors for instance? We have seen that the behaviour of conduction electrons is different in a superconductor from in a normal metal. They can be said to behave in a more orderly way in the superconductor. Now the second law of thermodynamics associates orderliness with a reduction of entropy, or, supposing temperatures to be kept constant, with a reduction of energy. But suppose there is a way of making the already ordered electrons of a superconductor go into disorder: they will have to get energy from somewhere, in fact from the lattice of atoms, by absorbing some of the phonons. There is indeed a very simple way of disordering the electrons of a superconductor—by switching on a magnetic field sufficient to destroy its superconductivity. When this is done to superconducting tantalum at 2°K, for instance, with a field of 1,000 gauss, the tantalum drops to 0·5°K; and if it started from 1°K it would drop to about 0·1°K. Unfortunately neither the electrons nor the lattices have large enough specific heats at these temperatures to make this type of cooling attractive. The tantalum, for instance, warms up again through leakage of heat before any useful measurements can be made on it.

The Lowest Energy Levels

So far we are therefore inclined to reject the idea either of a direct attack on the phonon quantum numbers or of using conduction electrons in superconductors as intermediaries, in our desire to perform measurements and experiments in the temperature range 0·3°K to 0·0003°K. What else can be got into such a low energy state that it will absorb phonons from a lattice which is already very cold indeed? Let us consider those many electrons which are bound within the atoms. They are not completely bound, after all, and they can possess four kinds of energy.

First there are the energies an electron may have according to its distance from the nucleus. All the possible energies are proportional to $-1/1^2$, $-1/2^2$, $-1/3^2$, etc., getting nearer to zero as the distance increases, until for large distances the energy is practically zero. These energy values are negative in agreement with the fact that energy must be supplied to the electron in order to remove it from the atom. The whole numbers in this case are called *principal* quantum numbers. The energies are similar to the angular momentum of a planet going round its orbit, and smaller differences in energy are possible, corresponding to the different possible ellipticities of the orbit. These, too, are quantized in terms of whole numbers, which are called the *auxiliary* quantum numbers. The third and fourth kinds of energy difference occur only if there is a magnetic field. Number three is associated with the angle between the plane of the orbit and the direction of the field. It has values proportional to any negative or positive whole number, provided this is not larger than the auxiliary quantum number of the particular electron to which it refers. The new number is called the *magnetic* quantum number, and it must be multiplied by H, the strength of the magnetic field. Notice particularly that H can be varied at the will of the experimenter, so he can directly control the size of the magnetic quantum jumps. The same is true of the fourth and last, called the *spin* quantum number, with which we had a fleeting encounter earlier in this chapter. This is associated with the magnetic effect of a spinning electron, and it can have only two values, either $+\frac{1}{2}$ or $-\frac{1}{2}$, as if the spinning electron is a small magnet which must align itself either along the field, or directly against it. The magnetic and spin quantum numbers of an electron in an atom are often added together, which is like adding the angular momentum of the orbital motion of a planet to the angular momentum of its own spin. The combined number always ends in an add $\frac{1}{2}$, and called the *angular momentum*, J. A remarkably effective way of cooling materials below 1°K hangs on manipulations of the energy levels of angular momentum.

Fig. 16.2, left-hand side, shows the energy levels of those electrons in a crystal for which $\mathcal{J} = 5/2$. The electrons could be in a zero field, but it is easier to suppose they are in a very small magnetic field, and therefore the energy levels are close together. If the crystal is at a temperature of 1°K there are plenty of phonons capable of moving the electrons from one level to another. The equal thick lines at the right of the level markers represent the fact, therefore, that equal numbers of electrons are in all

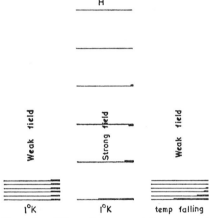

Fig. 16.2. Effect of demagnetizing a crystal.

six states. Equal numbers, that is, have their angular momentums oriented in each of six different directions in relation to the direction of the small external magnetic field.

Now, if a much larger external field is switched on, the levels widen out as in the centre part of the figure; and initially there still are equal numbers of electrons in all levels. This situation does not persist, however, for the electrons in the upper levels now have more energy than the lattice phonons and they drop to lower levels, generating some relatively big phonons as they go. Soon a new equilibrium is reached between the "magnetic" electrons and the lattice phonons, but the temperature of the crystal will now be considerably higher than 1°K—there are more and bigger phonons. But if the extra phonons are removed by recooling the crystal to 1°K, the magnetic electrons take advantage of this outflow of heat to make some more jumps down from higher levels, and their numbers in the lower levels are very much greater than in the upper levels. The thickened lines in the centre part of the figure represent the proportions of electrons in the different levels, with the big field switched on and the crystal recooled to 1°K.

Finally, let the large field be switched off, leaving only the original small field. The energy levels close in again, but initially most of the magnetic electrons are in the very lowest levels as in the right hand side of the figure, and there are still phonons in the lattice corresponding to 1°K. Many of these phonons are absorbed within a few minutes by the magnetic electrons, raising them into higher levels, and making their distribution among the levels approach that on the left of the figure. The loss of so many phonons means a substantial reduction of the crystal temperature, and the final temperature at which the magnetic electrons and phonons are in equilibrium may be lower than 0·1°K. By using a starting temperature of a few tenths of a degree, even lower temperatures, less than 0·01°K, can be reached.

Cooling by Demagnetization

This method of cooling really works in practice. The apparatus needed is a mixture of the delicate and the gross. First there is the crystal, about which more must be written later. Round it there is a metal can which contains traces of helium gas, to be evacuated before the final demagnetization. Round the can is another metal can which is filled with liquid helium and pumped very fast to cool it to 1°K. Round the second can is a third can, with the space between evacuated so that the two together form a Dewar vessel. Round the three cans is a glass Dewar containing ordinary liquid helium or hydrogen to protect them from any inflow of heat. The glass Dewar is quite big, about half a gallon in capacity, but it tapers at the bottom to dimensions only just large enough to surround the three cans, about 2 in. outside diameter. Its fatter part contains reserves of cold liquid. The levels of the top and bottom of the crystal are marked on the outside of the narrow part of the glass Dewar. While the crystal is cooling down a big electromagnet on a trolley, of total weight about 5 cwt, is wheeled into position so that the crystal is centrally between its iron pole pieces. The field is switched on and cooling continues until the crystal is at 1°K. The trace of helium gas which has been conducting heat away from the crystal is now pumped away from the innermost can, and the field switched off and the magnet wheeled away. Within a few minutes the crystal is found to have a temperature of about 0·1°K and still falling.

Fig. 16.3 shows the arrangement of the crystal and the cans round it. The serrated black areas represent the copper coils

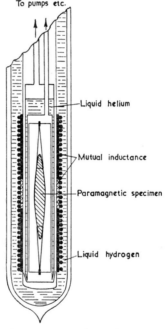

Fig. 16.3. Apparatus for cooling to 0.01°K.

which are used to measure the temperature of the crystal by determining its magnetic properties.

The material of the crystal has to be chosen very carefully. Only about one fiftieth of the atoms should have a "magnetic electron", because the natural magnetic fields of these electrons must not influence each other—otherwise their orientations would be determined by the fields of their neighbours instead of by the external magnetic field. For example, iron ammonium alum with its twelve molecules of water of crystallization has the formula $FeNH_4(SO_4)_2.12H_2O$; and the iron atom, Fe, is the only one with a magnetic electron. In every molecule there is one iron atom and 51 others. Another essential property is that in a magnetic field of a few thousand gauss (oersteds) the separation of the energy levels is greater than the energy of phonons at $1°K$. Iron ammonium alum has this property also, together with about a dozen other salts. Cerium magnesium nitrate is better at still lower starting temperatures.

The crystal specimen should be a long ellipsoid, 1 cm or less in diameter and two or three cm (about an inch) long. It can be made from a single crystal, or from powder pressed into shape and sealed with a film of nail varnish to prevent the water of crystallization from evaporating away during storage.

Coldest Of All

To reach still lower temperatures, materials must be found in which there are even smaller angular momenta than those of electrons in orbit. This is not difficult, for the nucleus of every atom containing an odd number of protons has a "spin", which is quantized according to the usual rules of quantum theory. Secondly, the material should have rapid means of energy exchange between the lattice and the nuclei, so that when the magnetic field is removed and the nuclei fall into abnormally low energy levels, phonons from the lattice can be absorbed as the nuclei ascend into slightly higher energy levels. Luckily, metals have the necessary property, because their conduction electrons (which carry electric currents so easily) are able to absorb energy from phonons and give it to nuclei, and vice versa. The greatest technical difficulty is the size of magnetic field needed to increase the separation of the nuclear energy levels and make it greater than the energy of the phonons. By keeping the phonons to a temperature of $0.01°K$, and by using fields of nearly 30,000 gauss, in 1956, at Oxford, Kurti, Robinson, Simon and Spohr cooled a specimen of copper to $0.00002°K$. Their magnet used about a fifth of the entire power of the Oxford electricity generating station. It could only be used at night, after the station engineers had prepared their plant for the rapid increase in power output as the current was switched on a step at a time.

Controlling the Direction of a Nucleus

As a result of the work on cooling by nuclear demagnetization, some valuable technical experience has been gained, but there have been no new discoveries about the effect of cold on matter. However, a useful experimental technique has come into being, for which nuclear physicists in particular should be grateful. They need to know more about the stages of radioactive decay, which are different for each element; and they have plenty of radioactive elements to study, in the various products of neutron bombardment in their nuclear piles.

A really big magnetic field, as we have seen, will control the direction of any nucleus which has "spin." When cooling by demagnetization is not the aim, there is no need to harness a town's electricity supply to do this, because very strong but tiny magnetic fields exist already within the atom. It is sufficient to go through with the demagnetization of a crystal from a field of about 25,000 oersteds. When the field is switched off, a temperature of about 0·01°K is produced, but there are strong enough electric and magnetic forces between the atoms of the crystal for them to remain approximately aligned. The nuclei within these atoms follow suit, and they, too, remain approximately in line with the direction of the former external field. This is the situation needed for the experiment—a set of nuclei with their spins all nearly parallel.

The experiment, then, is to make radioactive nuclei align their spins in this manner, and wait for them to decay. A typical form of decay is for the nucleus to eject an electron (called a beta particle from a long historical association going back to the days of Mme Curie). This leaves the nucleus with one neutron changed to a proton, and it is at a high energy level. To get to the ground state, of lowest energy, it must emit one or more photons (called gamma rays in the historical parlance). Now comes the point of having the nuclei aligned. The gamma rays emerge in the direction of alignment if they are due to certain types of electron transition, and at right angles to this direction if they are due to other types. The nuclear physicist counts the numbers of gamma rays emerging in different directions, and uses this information to build up a picture of the nuclear energy levels, and the spins and parities associated with them.

Chapter Seventeen

ABSOLUTE ZERO AND BEYOND

ONE OF THE PURPOSES of this chapter will be to explain why absolute zero will never be reached. Such claims as this are in the province of the philosophers, and this is not a philosophical book. However, at Oxford physics is called natural philosophy (probably because this makes it easier to translate into Latin) and we shall use it as an excuse to go slightly philosophical.

For the entire nineteenth century physicists believed that absolute zero was unobtainable, for altogether the wrong reason. Using classical laws they reached two conclusions, both of which were extremely wrong. Both of them stated that something was infinite, which turned out later to be almost zero, so can anything be more wrong that that?

The more philosophical of the two false conclusions stated that to cool any material to absolute zero an infinite amount of work would have to be done on an ideal heat engine. If so, then presumably an infinite amount of work would be needed to cool it by the last thousandth of a degree (infinity cannot be divided). We now know, however, that the heat to be abstracted from any substance at 0·001°K, to cool it to absolute zero, is very small indeed; much smaller even than if the temperature change were from 0·001°C to 0·000°C. This makes it seem unlikely, to say the least, that an infinite amount of work would be needed. The modern view is that almost no work would be needed, but that the heat engine would have to go through an infinite number of cycles.

The other false conclusion concerned entropy. The entropy of any object is connected with the heat energy it contains, divided by its temperature in degrees Kelvin. If a small amount of heat dQ is put into an object whose temperature is T, its entropy increases by an amount dQ/T. The fact that its temperature changes at the same time to $T + dT$ is unimportant. A very simple piece of calculus shows that the entropy of any object obeying the classical laws would be minus infinity at the absolute zero of temperature.

The only way for this not to be true would be for the specific heat of the material to be zero at zero temperature, but classical theory requires that any solid has the same specific heat at all temperatures.

When Einstein applied quantum considerations to the specific heat of solids, he found that they all had to have zero specific heat at absolute zero, rising to steady constant values at high temperatures. (Later theoreticians have altered the shape of the rise more in accordance with observations, but this does not matter here.) When the entropy of a solid is calculated for absolute zero by Einstein's method or by any other quantum method, it works out to be zero and not minus infinity. So once again the classical view has to be drastically changed.

This change of view had a tremendous practical effect. For one thing the whole gamut of phenomena in the region of absolute zero became much more interesting to experimental physicists, and they performed the marvellous experiments at low temperatures on which modern low temperature physics is founded. Even more important, absolute zero became the ideal reference point for measurements in thermochemistry. Manufacturing chemists need to know whether any two materials will react to form a third, fourth or fifth material, and if so what is the best temperature and pressure at which to use them. The designers of their plant work with measurements of the specific heat of each pure substance at all temperatures down to absolute zero, and with heats of combustion. With these data they calculate the free-energy change of the chemical reaction in which they are interested. If this works out to a satisfactory value, they go ahead and design the plant in detail. But if their calculations are wrong, even by a relatively small amount, the consequences may be disastrous. In the 1960s it was reported that two chemical plants for the production of boron compounds had to be shut down prematurely, mainly because erroneous and incomplete data had been used for their design. The cost of building each plant had been 38 million dollars·

The Third Law of Thermodynamics

Absolute zero became the reference point for thermochemists, and made calculation possible (whether right or wrong), in 1906 when a new law was postulated by Nernst in Berlin. This later became known as the Third Law of thermodynamics. Like the

Second Law, it may be expressed in various ways. In its original form it read "At the absolute zero all changes of state take place at constant entropy".

Unfortunately it soon earned a poor reputation in this form, because there are obvious exceptions. For example, measurements showed quite clearly that if glass were made to change its state at absolute zero, from the super-cooled amorphous substance which we know to a perfect crystal, there would be a lowering of its entropy. The law only applied to materials in internal equilibrium, with no strain of any kind. We have seen how the magnetic energy levels of the electrons in a crystal can be influenced by an external magnetic field, and how time is needed for them to get into equilibrium with the phonons of the lattice vibrations. The magnetic electrons together form what is called a component of the thermodynamic system, i.e. in this case of the pure crystal. Other components, such as F-centres and magnetic nucleons may be present as well, in addition to the lattice itself which is usually the main component. A modern version of the Third Law states "The contribution to the entropy of a system due to each component which is in internal equilibrium disappears at absolute zero". This formulation neatly takes care of all known "exceptions", and provides a basis for the chemists with which they are completely satisfied.

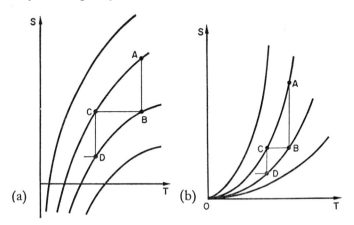

Fig. 17.1. Entropy (a) of a "classical" system, and (b) of a "quantum" system obeying the Third Law.

The unattainability of absolute zero follows from the Third Law. The changes in any system which would be needed to reach this goal simply cannot be carried out. Fig. 17.1 (a and b) shows the wrong and right suppositions about how entropy (S) varies at very low temperatures. The family of 4 curves represents the entropy under four values of some external influences (for instance pressure or magnetic field). The step, ABCD, indicates how cooling may be effected by zig-zagging from one value to another. On the left, according to the classical model, the specimen would zig-zag towards $S = -\infty$; on the right, according to the quantum model, it zig-zags towards $S = 0$. In neither case can it ever reach zero temperature.

Negative Temperature

The claim is sometimes made that a newly discovered optical device, the laser, is an example of how a thermodynamic system may have one of its components at a negative temperature. Incredible as this may seem, it really means a temperature of less than absolute zero. Since it is made by reputable scientists, the claim will have to be very carefully examined. What is the principle of the laser? What has it to do with temperature? Does it affect the unattainability of absolute zero, or the Third Law? Neither scientific nor philosophical opinion has yet settled down into a uniform "feeling", so the views now to be given are very personal and tentative. The whole matter is so interesting, however, that some discussion of it is desirable, and almost any view is better than none at all.

The acronym L.a.s.e.r. stands for Light Amplification by Stimulated Emission of Radiation. Lasers can be made with pure gases or crystals. Fig. 17.2 illustrates how a ruby laser works. Ruby is a crystal of aluminium oxide containing a small percentage of chromium oxide which is responsible for its deep red colour. The ruby in the figure, a manufactured one, has its crystal axis along the axis of the cylinder, and both ends are coated with reflecting silver. The right-hand end has only a thin layer of silver, because the final pulse of Radiation has to come out at this end, travelling exactly along the line of the axis.

Round the ruby is a spiral glass tube containing the rare gas xenon which gives a brilliant whitish green light flash when a strong current is pulsed through between the electrodes at the

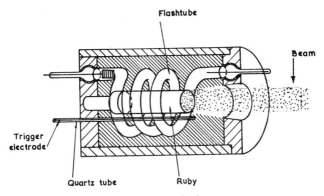

Fig. 17.2. A ruby laser.

ends. The flashes are made as rapidly as possible. As their purpose is to be absorbed by the ruby, the assembly is enclosed in a reflecting can with a circular opening in the middle of the right-hand end. After a measured amount of light energy has been absorbed by the ruby (in about half a minute's flashing), an electrical impulse is sent by the operator along a trigger electrode. Immediately, a tremendously strong flash of infra-red radiation shoots out from the right-hand end of the ruby. It is not really visible, but is accompanied by a deep red light.

The total energy in the laser flash may be as much as 50 calories (210 joules), enough to boil nearly $\frac{3}{4}$ gramme of water. Not much of a total, perhaps, but it is all released in 1–2 milliseconds. For this brief period, the power is equivalent to several thousand 100 watt lamps. The first lesson which must be learnt by the experimenter is to keep out of the way of laser flashes, and especially to avoid getting them in the eyes, whose lenses would focus them on to a very small area of the retina. If a laser flash is focussed on to a $\frac{1}{8}$ in. steel plate it will puncture a hole right through it. The laser will soon become an important practical device, with military, medical, telecommunication, and research applications. A large number of laboratories are struggling to find the best materials and most effective designs for making them.

Fig. 17.3 shows why there is a giant light flash from a laser. The xenon radiation first raises a large number of lattice atoms

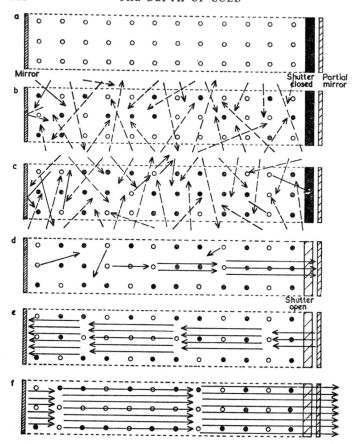

Fig. 17.3. Explanation of a laser.

from their lowest energy level (ground state) to a particular
energy level, which will be called the excited state, as in strips
(a) and (b). Every arrow represents a photon. Strip (c) shows this
process continuing, and some of the excited atoms are falling back
to the ground state, emitting photons as they do so. Xenon radiation is shown with broken arrows, and emitted radiation with full
arrows. It is a feature of ruby, and other laser materials, that most
of the atoms remain excited for many seconds; but that their fall

back to the ground state can be "triggered" by radiation of the same wavelength as they emit during that fall. At strip (d) the black absorbing material on the right has been removed, leaving the thin layer of silver to reflect back any emitted radiation reaching it, particularly that which travels exactly along the crystal axis. Strips (e) and (f) show how the emitted photons grow in number as they trigger off excited atoms en route. Finally they all burst through the thin layer of silver, in the same millisecond, in the same direction, and in step (all their vibrations are in the same phase together). The result is a burst of radiation whose intensity and coherence is very much greater than anything else we have achieved.

What has this phenomenon to do with temperature? We look at it from the point of view of energy levels. In Fig. 17.4 the line

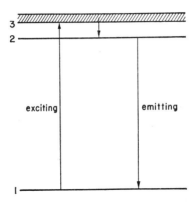

Fig. 17.4. Energy diagram of a ruby laser.

labelled (1) is the lowest energy level of an electron in an atom, the ground state. When an atom absorbs a photon from the xenon radiation one of its electrons increases its distance from the nucleus and rises to level (3). This has been drawn as a band, rather than a thin line, because there are numerous energy levels, any one of which the electron quickly drops to an exact energy level (2). Its energy loss is accompanied by a phonon or photon of equal energy but since level (3) is a band the precise amount of

energy is not predictable and therefore this transition is not particularly interesting. Level (2), however, is extremely interesting
because the energy of the electron is both precise and metastable
—i.e. the electron stays at level (2) until it is triggered somehow
into falling back to level (1). The triggering may happen casually
through thermal motion (phonons), or through an electrical force
such as externally imposed potential difference, or through an
electromagnetic field if a photon of the right wavelength passes
that way.

Now temperature is also a matter of energy levels, at least from
one point of view. When a crystal is in temperature equilibrium
at temperature $T°$K; if we consider any two of the energy levels
its atoms may be in, and suppose the energies are E_m and E_n;
then we can calculate the ratio of the numbers of atoms having
each of the two energies. If the numbers are N_m and N_n the
formula is:

$$N_m/N_n = \exp\left(-(E_m - E_n)/kT\right)$$

where k is Boltzmann's constant. When E_m and E_n are the same,
the right-hand side is exp(0) or e^0 which is 1; that is $N_m = N_n$.
If E_m is greater than E_n, the right-hand side is less than 1, which
means that N_m is less than N_n. This is what would be expected,
for it is reasonable that there should always be more atoms in the
lower of the two energy levels.

If we suppose the two energy levels are fixed, as they are in
practice, we can vary the ratio N_m/N_n only by varying T. If T
is $0°$K, the ratio is 0, i.e. all the atoms are in the lower level,
consistent with our ideas of absolute zero. At all other values of
T, there are some atoms in the level E_m because the ratio is
greater than 0. Finally, if T is infinite, the right-hand side again
becomes exp(0) which is 1. Thus $N_m = N_n$ only at an infinite
temperature.

The atoms in a crystal have many energy levels, of course, and
the formula applies to all of them—it gives the ratio of the
numbers of atoms in any pair of levels we like to choose. The
distributions of Fig. 16·1 in the last chapter were calculated
by it.

So far, only one way of altering the numbers in different energy
levels has been considered—by changing the temperature. But in
laser techniques and related work there is another way, by forcing

the atoms to absorb the energy of light. In Fig. 17.3 the atoms in their ground state were represented by open circles, and in their excited state by black circles. In strips (c) and (d), there were more black circles shown than open circles, and this is not a mistake, for it can happen. Now let us suppose there is a crystal whose atoms have only two energy levels, and by means of a xenon lamp we put more than half the atoms into the upper level. What is the temperature of the crystal? The formula we have just been using presumably is still applicable, but this time we put values into the left-hand side. Very well, suppose we have a crystal for which N_m/N_n is 2·7 (this happens to be e approximately). Then the formula shows that $-(E_m - E_n)/kT = 1$. Therefore, $kT = -(E_m - E_n)$. Remember that E_m is greater than E_n, so kT must be negative. Boltzmann's constant k is a fixed positive number, so we are left with the result that T is negative! This sounds ridiculous, but at least it is consistent with our former calculations which showed that, as T moved from 0°K right up to infinity, the ratio N_m/N_n moved from 0 to 1.

Negative temperature! All sorts of questions spring to mind, but all the answers seem rather dampening, without actually proving that the whole idea is nonsense. Here are some of them arranged as a sort of quiz.

Q. What would happen if the ruby crystal were given the xenon flashes until N_m became greater than N_n, and then it were held in the hand? A. Nothing. It would feel the same as if a glass rod had been picked up at the temperature of the room.

Q. Would it be possible to use the negative temperature of the atoms in a ruby to absorb the phonons in its lattice and so, perhaps, cool the crystal itself down towards absolute zero? A. No. To change the temperature of the atoms back to normal, those at level (2) must drop down to level (1). In doing so, they give out energy as a photon. It is quite feasible for this photon to be absorbed by the lattice and converted into phonons, but this would increase the temperature of the crystal as a whole and not lower it.

Q. Isn't this contrary to commonsense? It seems as if something which has a temperature less than zero has more energy than if its temperature were zero. A. Yes it has more energy. Remember that energy was put into the ruby to make N_m, the number of atoms at level (2), greater than N_n. At one stage N_m must have just equalled N_n, and the formula shows that the temperature was then infinite. After that, even more energy was put into the ruby to make the temperature negative.

Q. It seems that the temperature has gone right through infinity in order to go negative. Is this plausible? A. Perfectly plausible. Consider for example Fig. 17.5. The curve is a rectangular

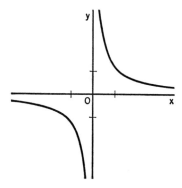

Fig. 17.5. Rectangular hyperbola.

hyperbola with the equation $xy = 1$, and it is a simple curve with no singularities. As x diminishes from 1 towards zero, the value of y increases until the curve disappears out of the top of the diagram. Only when x has passed right through zero does the curve reappear, and then it is at the bottom of the diagram, so y is negative. Clearly y has not gone through zero to reach these negative values; it must have gone through infinity.

Q. Does this imply a breakdown of the Second Law? If the temperature can jump from high positive values to high negative values, mustn't entropy do the same? A. No. the Second Law still holds. The entropy is the integral of dQ/T, as the temperature is raised by adding small amounts of energy, dQ at a time. In our case the integration is best done in two stages, first from the positive temperature to infinity, and then from minus infinity to the negative temperature. Both contributions are positive, and the entropy of the system (i.e. of the atoms in relation to the two energy levels being considered) is not negative at any stage, but it increases throughout.

Q. Presumably the Third Law is not affected either? A. The Third Law is about absolute zero, and that is one temperature which even the fluorescent-atom component of a crystal cannot achieve.

Q. Since the numbers of atoms in levels (1) and (2) can be manipulated, why can't they all be brought into level (1), and so make this component go to absolute zero? A. All the manipulation that has been done so far has achieved the raising of atoms from level (1) to level (2). No method of artificially lowering a level has been found. As a matter of fact, at room temperature, in the dark, the proportion of ruby atoms at level (2) is very small indeed, but even these few can't be dealt with by any known means.

Q. Can any further comment be made about the unattainability of absolute zero? A. It still seems to be unattainable, but the proof of this is no longer unassailable. The proof is based on a thermodynamic argument. It has not covered the possibility of getting at individual excited atoms, though it probably could.

Q. The idea of infinite temperature isn't easy to accept, is it? A. The idea of using a finite amount of energy to raise even one component of a system to infinite temperature is novel, to say the least. There is no possibility of a gas being heated to such a temperature, for its molecules would have to have infinite velocity, and there is not enough energy in the whole universe to do that. The specific heat of gases does not go down at high temperatures; on the contrary it increases because of the relativistic increase in the mass of its molecules. The system of fluorescent atoms, on the other hand, must have a specific heat which approaches zero as its temperature approaches infinity.

Q. Wouldn't it be simple to avoid these difficulties by saying that the idea of temperature is not applicable to atoms in an optically excited state? A. There would be great difficulty in justifying such a statement but it might be worth investigating. We should have to look at the combination kT which appeared in the formula earlier in this chapter. It is a combination which, though it started in the classical kinetic theory, now pervades the whole of quantum physics. It first occurred there in Planck's radiation formula, which correctly described in 1900, for the first time, what sort of radiation could be in equilibrium with a black body of temperature T.

Q. But we are now far beyond the stage of black bodies ? A. True. We have gone from black bodies to separate components of a system, and from radiation to excited atoms. While it is always possible to calculate how many atoms are excited in a body at any temperature, it is only exceptionally possible to find the temperature which corresponds to an actual number of excited atoms. This is because there is usually more than one excited state (two were shown in Fig. 17.4 but we conveniently forgot about level (3)).

Here is a job for the philosophers, the Natural Philosophers whose predecessors many years ago started to make the study of science respectable at Oxford and other highly scholastic universities. There seems to be a paradox, a situation where the evidence appears contradictory though this is ridiculous in the light of common sense. The most famous paradox, of Achilles and the Tortoise, seemed to prove that if Achilles started the race anywhere behind the tortoise he would never catch up, because the process of catching up could be divided into an infinite number of steps (the distance between them being halved, then halved again, then halved again, and so on to infinity). The difficulty was not resolved until ways had been found of summing the infinite series, and the sum was found to be finite.

The paradox about temperature is much more complicated. Common sense wants any rise in temperature to be roughly proportional to the amount of heat or energy put in. On this basis a good scale of temperature has been devised which works effectively from absolute zero, when the body has no heat in it, to the hottest temperatures which can be reached in furnaces, nuclear plasmas and explosions, and, as far as we know, in heavenly bodies. The idea of heating up any body to an infinite temperature is out of the question, because the necessary energy would be infinite.

Unfortunately for common sense, there was a difficulty in explaining the wavelengths of radiation from a hot body. When a quite reasonable approach to this problem was made in Cambridge by Rayleigh and Jeans, it predicted that there should be an impossibly large amount of short-wave radiation. The only way out of the difficulty was Planck's introduction of the quantum of energy, in 1900, and it must at once be said that this has led to enormous progress in the explanation of the properties of atoms and other particles as well as of radiation. Even if it should ultimately turn out not to be absolutely the best way of looking at atomic physics, it has produced such a huge pay-off in science and technology that Planck 1900 should be given as great a place in history as Columbus 1492.

However, wherever the quantum of energy, h, occurs in a formula, it brings with it T, and T is a temperature. Scientists were quite happy in the early days when T had just to be the absolute temperature of a body which was giving off radiation, and equally pleased later when T was the absolute temperature of any form of matter in thermal equilibrium. They gulped a little when offered the idea of T being the temperature of a separate aspect of matter, such as the electrons in certain "orbits" in the atoms of a gas or a crystal—but most of them swallowed it. Then they found that the practical possibility of a negative temperature, and its realization too, followed inevitably. Equally logical and practical, but even more horrifying, was the idea of infinite temperature. And now where is common sense? A separate aspect of matter, such as a selection from the electrons in a ruby, can be given an infinite temperature by employing only a finite amount of energy. Must there be exceptions to the dictum that if the temperature is infinite, the energy needed is infinite also? Once exceptions are allowed, the whole structure of reasoning may crumble. It is better to admit that there is a clear paradox and hope that a future generation of philosophers and physicists will put it right.

INDEX